D1624807

Foundations of Real Numbers

Foundations of Real Numbers

CLAUDE W. BURRILL
New York University

McGRAW-HILL BOOK COMPANY   *New York   St. Louis*
San Francisco   Toronto   London   Sydney

Foundations of Real Numbers

Library of Congress Catalog Card Number 67-19145

09224

1234567890 MAMM 7432106987

to O. A. B. *and* K. R. F. B

Preface

This book is written for the mature undergraduate or beginning graduate student who wishes to learn about the foundations of the real number system. It provides him with what I believe to be the necessary and sufficient information: a concise development of the real numbers from a foundation of set theory, a proof that the real numbers are unique, and a discussion of the two classical definitions due to Dedekind and to Cantor.

The traditional approach to real numbers requires as a preliminary that the rational numbers be constructed from the integers. This is not a difficult operation but one that involves dealing with equivalence classes and requires a fair amount of detail. With the rationals at hand, the real numbers themselves are taken to be Dedekind cuts or, in the Cantor approach, equivalence classes of sequences. While the student should be aware of these traditional methods, it is unfortunately true that neither of the classical definitions is close to the student's intuitive notion of a real number. Instead of following this line, the primary construction of real numbers in this book is directly from the integers. This shortens the path from set theory to real numbers; more important, the construction is a very natural one since it is based directly on the decimal representation of real numbers which is, after all, the way most people view them.

The book is designed as a text and is suitable for a one-semester course; it may be used also for collateral reading or independent study. It contains well over 100 exercises, many of which are designed to extend the material of the text.

The reader who desires only a proof of the existence and uniqueness of the real numbers may omit Chapters 8 and 9 and the Appendix; alternatively, he may omit Chapter 6 and read instead the Appendix and either Chapter 8 or Chapter 9.

Using a modest version of a symbol introduced by Halmos, I have indicated the end of a proof by ▲.

I am indebted to many colleagues for helpful comments; especially I wish to thank J. R. Knudsen, M. J. Meisner, and I. F. Ritter.

Claude W. Burrill

Contents

Preliminaries

Chapter One
Preliminaries

1 INTRODUCTION

Real numbers are so much a part of our daily experience that we often overlook the centuries of effort that went into their creation. This evolution began in prehistoric times when the positive integers arose naturally from man's need to count and, later, to conduct trade. The ancients added a rudimentary knowledge of fractions, although for centuries mankind largely avoided such quantities through the expedient of splitting fundamental units into smaller units; the division of the pound into ounces and the ounce into pennyweights is an example of this tendency. Use of the number zero did not appear until the ninth century, while negative numbers were not fully recognized and understood until about the seventeenth. The lateness of these dates gives some indication of the profound difficulties encountered in conceiving the real numbers as they are known today.

Although their existence was recognized by the ancient Greeks, irrational numbers were a source of mystery and confusion right up to the end of the nineteenth century. At that time various writers, of whom Richard Dedekind and Georg Cantor were foremost, showed how such quantities can be defined in terms of rational numbers. This discovery finally enabled mathematicians to give precise meanings to concepts such as limit and continuity, thereby paving the way for the rapid development of analysis witnessed in the twentieth century.

With the emergence of a satisfactory theory of irrational numbers, investigation next turned to the foundations of the number system. Until that time it had been assumed without question that the natural numbers [that is, the numbers 0, 1, . . .] were the simplest and most basic of all mathematical entities and were, therefore, the foundation of the real number system. Then in 1901 Giuseppe Peano discovered that the natural numbers themselves could be derived from a more fundamental system; as a result they were assigned a secondary role, and for many years the Peano axioms were considered to be the primary source of all mathematical knowledge.

Peano's discovery and, prior to that, the introduction of set theory by Cantor spurred investigators to delve still deeper into the foundations of mathematics, and soon the relation of mathematics to logic itself was being examined. During the first part of the twentieth century, Bertrand Russell popularized the notion that mathematics is a branch of logic and supported this contention by defining the natural numbers in terms of concepts of logic. At about the same time, Ernst Zermelo led a movement to revamp set theory by introducing an axiomatic formulation in place of the naïve approach used by Cantor. This movement was aided by John von Neumann, one of whose contributions is the definition of natural numbers appearing in Chapter 2. Present-day mathematical logic has emerged as a blend of axiomatic set theory and the logical calculus.

Open questions concerning the foundations of mathematics still exist, although today such problems are of more interest to the mathematical logician than to a person dealing strictly with mathematics. It is now recognized that the various paradoxes of set theory that were discovered at the turn of the century do not occur when one is dealing exclusively with the sets that arise in mathematics, that is, sets of integers, sets of real numbers, sets of functions of real numbers, etc. Because of this, a completely uncritical theory of sets combined with the rules of symbolic logic serves as a satisfactory basis for most mathematical investigations. In the pages to follow we shall begin with such a basis, use it to develop the system of integers, and proceed from there to the construction of the real number system.

2 ALGEBRA OF SETS

Since most readers will have some familiarity with *set theory*, or at least with that type referred to as *naïve set theory*, we begin with but a brief review of this topic, emphasizing the parts that will be most useful in the sequel. No attempt will be made to analyze language or logic nor to discuss the meaning of terms such as "statement," "true," "false," "rule," and indeed "meaning" itself. In fact, no attempt will be made to define the word *set;* this will be taken as a basic concept in terms of which other quantities will be defined. Likewise the notion of *belonging to* a set or being a *member* or *element* of a set will be left undefined. If x belongs to a set A, we write $x \in A$; otherwise, $x \notin A$. If both x and y are members of A, it will be convenient to express this by writing $x, y \in A$. To avoid monotony, sometimes the word *collection* will be employed as a synonym for set.

Frequently a set is specified by some variant of the symbol $\{x: \ S(x)\}$, where $S(x)$ is some statement or sentence in which the letter x is "free." For example,

(1) $\qquad \{x: \ x$ is a positive integer less than $6\}$

specifies the set consisting of the integers 1, 2, 3, 4, and 5. A set consisting of a single member a is called a *singleton* and will frequently be denoted by $\{a\}$. A set consisting of exactly two members a and b is called a *pair* [or, for emphasis, an *unordered pair*] and is written $\{a,b\}$ or $\{b,a\}$. In the same way, we might write $\{3,1, 4,2,5\}$ for the set specified by (1).

Two sets A and B are *equal, $A = B$,* if they are identical. Thus $A = B$ means that $x \in A$ if and only if $x \in B$. Of course, we write $A \neq B$ if A and B are not equal. It is clear that the relation of equality of sets is *reflexive* [$A = A$], *symmetric* [$A = B$ implies $B = A$], and *transitive* [$A = B$ and $B = C$ imply $A = C$].

A set with no members is termed *empty.* It is easy to see that two empty sets are equal; accordingly we employ but one symbol, $\varnothing$, to signify any empty set. The reader should note that the sets $\varnothing$ and $\{\varnothing\}$ are not equal; the latter possesses the member $\varnothing$, while the former does not. Similarly, $\{\varnothing\} \neq \{\{\varnothing\}\}$. However, $\{\varnothing\} \in \{\{\varnothing\}\}$ is a correct statement, as is $\{\varnothing\} = \{\varnothing, \varnothing\}$.

A set A is a *subset* of a set B, $A \subset B$, if each member of A is a member of B. *Set inclusion* is *reflexive* [$A \subset A$], *transitive* [$A \subset B$ and $B \subset C$ imply $A \subset C$], and *antisymmetric* [$A \subset B$ and $B \subset A$ imply $A = B$]. Clearly $\varnothing \subset A$ for any set A. The notion of subset should not be confused with that of belonging to a set; for instance, $\varnothing \subset \varnothing$ but $\varnothing \notin \varnothing$.

A is a *proper* subset of B if $A \subset B$ and $A \neq B$. This means that each member of A is a member of B and that there is at least one member of B that is not in A.

Let $\mathcal{C}$ be a collection of sets. The *union* of the sets in $\mathcal{C}$ is written $\cup_{X \in \mathcal{C}} X$ and is defined to be the set $\{x: \ x \in X \text{ for some } X \in \mathcal{C}\}$. If $\mathcal{C}$ is a nonempty collection, the *intersection* of the sets in $\mathcal{C}$ is $\{x: \ x \in X \text{ for all } X \in \mathcal{C}\}$ and is denoted by $\cap_{X \in \mathcal{C}} X$. In case $\mathcal{C}$ consists of exactly two sets A and B, we write simply $A \cup B$ and $A \cap B$ for the union and intersection, respectively. Sets A and B are *disjoint* if $A \cap B = \varnothing$. We say that $\mathcal{C}$ is a *collection of disjoint sets* if A and B are disjoint for distinct $A, B \in \mathcal{C}$.

The *complement* of B with respect to A is the set

$$A - B = \{x: \ x \in A \text{ and } x \notin B\}.$$

If it is understood through context that the complement is with respect to some particular set S, then we write A^c for $S - A$.

The reader should satisfy himself as to the accuracy of the following basic facts.

(2)
$$A \cap (\cup_{X \in \mathcal{C}} X) = \cup_{X \in \mathcal{C}} (A \cap X).$$
$$A \cup (\cap_{X \in \mathcal{C}} X) = \cap_{X \in \mathcal{C}} (A \cup X).$$
$$(A^c)^c = A, \quad \varnothing^c = S, \quad S^c = \varnothing.$$
$$(\cup_{X \in \mathcal{C}} X)^c = \cap_{X \in \mathcal{C}} X^c.$$
$$(\cap_{X \in \mathcal{C}} X)^c = \cup_{X \in \mathcal{C}} X^c.$$
$$A - B = A \cap B^c.$$
$$A - (A - B) = A \cap B.$$
$$A \cap (B - C) = (A \cap B) - (A \cap C).$$

3 ORDERED PAIRS

The notion of an ordered pair is clear on intuitive grounds, but rather than add to our list of undefined concepts we give here a definition, due to Norbert Weiner, which is in terms of sets. Thus an *ordered pair* is a set (a,b) defined by

$$(a,b) = \{\{a\}, \{a,b\}\}.$$

The *first coordinate* of (a,b) is a; the *second coordinate* is b. That this formal definition agrees with an intuitive notion can be seen from the following.

Theorem 1

$(a,b) = (c,d)$ if and only if $a = c$ and $b = d$.

Proof Let us suppose that $(a,b) = (c,d)$ and show $a = c$ and $b = d$, the proof in the opposite direction being trivial.

Consider first the case $a = b$. In this event $(a,b) = \{\{a\}\}$. Since $\{c,d\} \in (a,b)$, $\{c,d\} = \{a\}$ so that $c = a$ and $d = a$. Hence $a = b = c = d$.

Next, consider the case $a \neq b$. Then it is not possible to have $\{c\} = \{a,b\}$, for this would imply $a = c$ and $b = c$, hence $a = b$. Since $\{c\} \in (a,b)$ and $\{c\} \neq \{a,b\}$, it follows that $\{c\} = \{a\}$, from which $c = a$. Also $\{a,b\} \in (c,d)$ and $\{a,b\} \neq \{c\}$ imply $\{a,b\} = \{c,d\}$. Thus $b = c$ or $b = d$; but the first of these is impossible for then $b = c = a$. We conclude that $a = c$ and $b = d$ ▲

The above concept can be used to introduce additional terms. We define an *ordered triple* (a,b,c) to be the ordered pair $((a,b),c)$ and an *ordered quadruple* (a,b,c,d) to be the ordered triple $((a,b),c,d)$. Also, from sets A and B the *cartesian product* $A \times B$ can be constructed. This is the collection of all ordered pairs with the first coordinate in A and the second in B; thus,

$$A \times B = \{(a,b): \ a \in A \text{ and } b \in B\}.$$

4 RELATIONS

For sets X and Y, a *relation* R *from* X *to* Y is a subset of the cartesian product $X \times Y$. We write $x \, R \, y$ in the event that $(x,y) \in R$ and say that x *stands* in the relation R to y. The *domain* and *range* of a relation have obvious meanings which can be expressed, respectively, by

$$\operatorname{dom} R = \{x: \ \text{for some } y, \ x \, R \, y\}$$

and

$$\operatorname{ran} R = \{y : \text{ for some } x, \, x \, R \, y\}.$$

Obviously, dom $R \subset X$ and ran $R \subset Y$.

Two trivial relations from X to Y are the sets $\varnothing$ and $X \times Y$. Clearly dom $\varnothing = $ ran $\varnothing = \varnothing$, while dom $X \times Y = X$ and ran $X \times Y = Y$ if both X and Y are nonempty. A more interesting relation is $R = \{(x.y) : \, x \in X, \, y \in Y, \text{ and } x = y\}$. Here $x \, R \, y$ if and only if $x = y$. This relation is merely the empty set if $X \cap Y = \varnothing$.

Frequently the domain and range of a relation are contained in the same set X, in which case the relation is said to be *in X*. A relation in X is *reflexive* if $x \, R \, x$ for each $x \in X$. It is *symmetric* if $x \, R \, y$ implies $y \, R \, x$, and it is *transitive* if $x \, R \, y$ and $y \, R \, z$ imply $x \, R \, z$. A relation may have none of the above properties or any combination of them, and the reader is invited to supply examples to illustrate the various possibilities.

An *equivalence* relation is one that is reflexive, symmetric, and transitive. Such a relation is usually denoted by $\sim$; thus we write $x \sim y$ and say x is *equivalent* to y if and only if $(x,y) \in \sim$. In this notation the properties of an equivalence relation are the following:

(a) $\quad x \sim x$,

(b) $\quad x \sim y$ implies $y \sim x$, and

(c) $\quad x \sim y$ and $y \sim z$ imply $x \sim z$.

If y is a member of a set X on which an equivalence relation $\sim$ is defined, the *equivalence class* determined by y is the subset C_y of X consisting of all members that are equivalent to y; that is,

$$C_y = \{x : \, x \in X \text{ and } x \sim y\}.$$

Clearly y itself is a member of C_y. Further, as we next show, equivalent elements determine the same equivalence class.

Theorem 2

$y \sim z$ if and only if $C_y = C_z$.

Proof Suppose that y and z are equivalent. If $x \in C_y$, then $x \sim y$ and, by transitivity, $x \sim z$ so that $x \in C_z$. Thus $C_y \subset C_z$. In a similar manner, $C_z \subset C_y$; it follows that $C_y = C_z$.

Next assume that $C_y = C_z$. Since $y \in C_y$, it follows that $y \in C_z$; hence $y \sim z$ ▲

Corollary

$$C_y = C_z \text{ or } C_y \cap C_z = \varnothing.$$

Proof Suppose that $x \in C_y$ and $x \in C_z$. Then $x \sim y$ and $x \sim z$. Hence $y \sim z$, and $C_y = C_z$ follows from the theorem ▲

As a result of the above statements, we see that the collection of all equivalence classes of X is a *partition* of that set, meaning that each element of X belongs to one and only one equivalence class. Further, it is easy to see that elements are in the same class if and only if they are equivalent.

A relation R in X is *antisymmetric* if $x \, R \, y$ and $y \, R \, x$ imply $x = y$. A reflexive, antisymmetric, and transitive relation is called a *partial order* or, simply, an *order;* it is usually denoted by the symbol $\leq$. Thus one writes $x \leq y$ and says that x is *less than or equal to y* if and only if (x,y) is a member of the partial order $\leq$. In this symbolism the above properties of a partial order become

(a) $x \leq x$,

(b) $x \leq y$ and $y \leq x$ imply $x = y$, and

(c) $x \leq y$ and $y \leq z$ imply $x \leq z$.

For a partial order, the fact that $x \leq y$ is also expressed by writing $y \geq x$ and saying that y is *greater than or equal to x*. Additionally, the symbols $x < y$ and $y > x$ are employed to signify that $x \leq y$ and $x \neq y$. It is said that x is *less than y* and that y is *greater than x* in case $x < y$.

An order in X is termed *linear* if, for $x,y \in X$, $x \leq y$ or $y \leq x$. The order relations encountered hereafter will all have this property. For a linear order it follows at once from antisymmetry that the *principle of trichotomy* applies; that is, for $x,y \in X$ exactly one of the following is true: $x < y$, $x = y$, $x > y$.

Let X be a set in which a linear order $\leq$ is defined, and let

B be a subset of X. A member a of X is a *lower bound* of B if $x \in B$ implies $a \leq x$. We say that b is the *minimum* of B and write $b = \min B$ if b is a lower bound of B and $b \in B$. Dually, d of X is an *upper bound* of B if $x \in B$ implies $x \leq d$; and c is the *maximum* of B, $c = \max B$, if c is an upper bound of B and $c \in B$. It is easy to see that the maximum and the minimum of a set are unique if they exist, but a set may have many lower and upper bounds.

The set B is *bounded below* if some lower bound of the set exists, that is, if the set L of lower bounds of B is not empty. If $\max L$ exists, it is denoted also by $\inf B$ and is called the *infimum* of B. Whenever the set B has a minimum, it is clear that $\min B$ is the greatest member of L, from which it follows that $\min B = \inf B$. However, there are important instances where the infimum of a set exists even though the minimum does not.

Dually, B is *bounded above* if some upper bound of the set exists. A set is *bounded* if it is bounded above and bounded below. If U, the set of upper bounds of B, has a minimum, then $\min U$ is also called the *supremum* of B and denoted $\sup B$. Whenever the maximum of a set exists, it is the supremum of the set.

5 FUNCTION

A relation f from X to Y is called a *function*, or a function from X *into* Y, if dom $f = X$ and if $(x,y) \in f$ and $(x,z) \in f$ imply $y = z$. In other words, f is a function from X into Y if for each $x \in X$ there is a unique $y \in Y$ such that $(x,y) \in f$. We write $f(x)$ for this unique y, refer to it as the *function value* or *image* of x, and say that f *assumes* the *value* $f(x)$ at x. Also, f is *defined* on X with *values* in Y. At times $x \to y$ or $x \to f(x)$ is used to display the connection between x and its image; in the same spirit, $X \to Y$ denotes the function itself.

Various synonyms are used for function, and we shall frequently employ *mapping* and *correspondence* in this way. Functions such as addition and multiplication from $X \times X$ into X are sometimes referred to as *operations*. It is convenient, although inaccurate, to describe such an operation as being *defined on* X even though the domain is $X \times X$.

If f and g are functions such that $\operatorname{dom} f \subset \operatorname{dom} g$ and $f(x) = g(x)$ for $x \in \operatorname{dom} f$, then g is an *extension* of f to the set $\operatorname{dom} g$, and f is a *restriction* of g to the set $\operatorname{dom} f$. It is easy to see that a function may be extended in many ways but that the restriction of a function to a particular set is unique.

A function f from X into Y is said to map *onto* Y, or to be from X *onto* Y, in case $\operatorname{ran} f = Y$. A function from X onto Y is called *one-to-one* and is a *one-to-one correspondence between X and Y* if distinct members of X have distinct images in Y, that is, if $x, z \in X$ and $f(x) = f(z)$ imply $x = z$. Thus a one-to-one correspondence is a pairing of the members of X with those of Y.

EXERCISES AND EXTENSIONS

1. Let $\mathfrak{U}$ be the set of all sets that do not belong to themselves. Does $\mathfrak{U}$ belong to itself? [The contradiction inherent in this situation is known as the *Russell paradox*, after Bertrand Russell who discovered it. This paradox shows that a naïve approach cannot be used to answer all questions in set theory.]

2. Verify the assertions of (2) in Article 2.

3. Give an example in which $A \times (B \times C) \neq (A \times B) \times C$.

4. Show that there is a natural correspondence between $A \times (B \times C)$ and $(A \times B) \times C$; between $(A \times B) \times (C \times D)$ and $((A \times B) \times C) \times D$.

5. Prove the following for sets A, B, C, and D.

    (a) $(A \cup B) \times C = (A \times C) \cup (B \times C)$.
    (b) $(A \cap B) \times (C \cap D) = (A \times C) \cap (B \times D)$.
    (c) $(A - B) \times C = (A \times C) - (B \times C)$.
    (d) $A \times B = \varnothing$ if and only if $A = \varnothing$ or $B = \varnothing$.

6. There are eight possible ways of classifying a relation, depending on whether it is reflexive or not, symmetric or not, and transitive or not. (a) Let $S = \{a, b, c\}$. Verify that the relation $R = \{(a,a),(b,b),(c,c),(b,c)\}$ in S is reflexive and transitive but is not symmetric. (b) Produce an example of a relation

in S that is reflexive and symmetric but is not transitive. (c) In the same way, find relations in S to illustrate the remaining six classifications.

7. Set inclusion is a relation in a collection of subsets. What are the properties of this relation?

8. Discuss the properties of the relations (a) "ancestor of," (b) "relation of," (c) "creditor of."

9. Give an example of a partial order that is not a linear order.

10. (a) List all functions from $X = \varnothing$ into Y. Does the answer depend on whether Y is empty? (b) Describe the set of functions from $X \neq \varnothing$ into $Y = \varnothing$.

If f is a function from X into Y and if g is a function from Y into Z, the *composite* function $h = g * f$ is defined from X into Z by $h(x) = g(f(x))$ for $x \in X$.

11. Show that the functions $j * (g * f)$ and $(j * g) * f$ are equal.

12. Is it possible to have $g * f = f * g$? Support your answer with a proof or an example.

13. Prove that if f is a one-to-one mapping from X onto Y and if g is a one-to-one mapping from Y onto Z, then $h = g * f$ is a one-to-one mapping from X onto Z.

If f is a one-to-one mapping from X onto Y, the *inverse mapping* f' is defined from Y into X by letting $f'(y) = x$ if and only if $f(x) = y$.

14. Prove that if f is a one-to-one mapping from X onto Y, then f' is a one-to-one mapping from Y onto X.

15. (a) Describe the function $f' * f$. (b) Is $f' * f = f * f'$?

A set A is *equivalent* to a set B and we write $A \sim B$ if there is a one-to-one mapping from A onto B.

16. Prove that equivalence of sets is an equivalence relation.

17. [*Bernstein's Theorem*] Prove that if A is equivalent to a subset of B, and if B is equivalent to a subset of A, then A is equivalent to B.

18. Assume that $A \subset B \subset C$ and $A \sim C$. Prove that $A \sim B$.

19. Assume that $A \sim B$, $a \in A$, and $b \in B$. Prove that $A - \{a\}$ and $B - \{b\}$ are equivalent.

Inductive Sets

Chapter Two
Inductive Sets

1 PEANO AXIOMS

In this chapter the concepts of set theory will be used to introduce a mathematical system that satisfies the *axioms of Peano*. Further properties of this system will be established in the next chapter, and when this is done we shall have constructed the system of natural numbers.

One of the basic properties of natural numbers is that for each such number there is a unique "successor" or "next" number; for instance, 3 is the successor of 2 and 7 is the successor of 6. It is not surprising that by knowing the successor of each number one can define an order relation on the natural numbers; it is not quite so obvious that with this knowledge one can also define addition and multiplication. It is with this notion of the "next" number that we shall be concerned in the present chapter, and the formal device for introducing the concept is the following.

For any set x, the *successor* of x is the set x' defined by

$$x' = x \cup \{x\}.$$

Thus $x \subset x'$ and $x \in x'$ are true statements for any set x. Also, $y \in x'$ if and only if $y \in x$ or $y = x$.

From the definition it can be seen that

$$\varnothing' = \{\varnothing\}$$
$$\{\varnothing\}' = \{\varnothing, \{\varnothing\}\}$$
$$\{\varnothing, \{\varnothing\}\}' = \{\varnothing, \{\varnothing\}, \{\varnothing, \{\varnothing\}\}\}$$

and so on. If, for the moment, we change notation and write 0 for $\varnothing$, 1 for $\varnothing'$, 2 for the successor of $\varnothing'$, etc., the above statements yield

$$0 = \varnothing$$
$$1 = 0' = \{0\}$$
$$2 = 1' = \{0,1\}$$
$$3 = 2' = \{0,1,2\}$$

and so on. Intuitively, 0 is a set with no members, 1 is a set with one member, etc. This new notation suggests that the natural numbers can be defined in terms of the successor and serves as motivation for what follows.

A set A is an *inductive set* if $\varnothing \in A$ and if $x \in A$ implies $x' \in A$. We shall assume the *axiom of infinity* to the effect that at least one inductive set exists; from this it is easy to show that there is a smallest set of this type.

Theorem 1

Let $\mathscr{I}$ be the collection of all inductive sets. Then

$$\omega = \bigcap_{A \in \mathscr{I}} A$$

is an inductive set.

Proof Note first that the axiom of infinity ensures that $\mathscr{I}$ is non-empty so that the intersection is defined. Since $\varnothing \in A$ for each $A \in \mathscr{I}$, it follows that $\varnothing \in \omega$. Suppose that $x \in \omega$. Then, for each $A \in \mathscr{I}$, $x \in A$ so that $x' \in A$. Hence $x' \in \omega$ ▲

Clearly ω as defined in Theorem 1 is the smallest inductive set in the sense that $\omega \subset A$ for any inductive set A. We call ω the *minimal* inductive set and the members of ω *natural numbers*.

The characteristic properties of natural numbers can be described by the five statements listed below; these are called the *Peano axioms*.

P1. $\varnothing \in \omega$.

P2. If $x \in \omega$, then $x' \in \omega$.

P3. If $x \in \omega$, then $x' \neq \varnothing$.

P4. If $A \subset \omega$, if $\varnothing \in A$, and if $x \in A$ implies $x' \in A$, then $A = \omega$.

P5. If $x, y \in \omega$ and if $x' = y'$, then $x = y$.

Properties *P1* and *P2* are immediate from the definition of inductive set. Since $x \in x'$ for any $x \in \omega$, it is clear that *P3* holds. Property *P4* is known as the *principle of mathematical induction*.

It follows from the fact that A is an inductive set so that $\omega \subset A$; hence $A = \omega$.

Before proving $P5$, it is useful to establish another property of the set ω.

Theorem 2

If $x \in \omega$ and if $z \in x'$, then $z \subset x$.

Proof Let

$$A = \{x: \ x \in \omega \text{ and if } z \in x', \text{ then } z \subset x\}.$$

The theorem will be proved by showing that A satisfies the hypotheses of $P4$. That $\varnothing$ is a member of A is true trivially. Suppose that $x \in A$ and let $z \in (x')'$. Then $z \in x'$ or $z = x'$. If $z \in x'$, then $z \subset x$ since $x \in A$; hence $z \subset x'$ since $x \subset x'$. If $z = x'$, then $z \subset x'$ is immediate. Thus $z \subset x'$ in both cases so that $x' \in A$ ▲

We are now in a position to prove $P5$. Let x and y be members of ω with $x' = y'$. Since $x \in x'$, $x \in y'$ so that $x \subset y$ by Theorem 2. In the same way, $y \subset x$. Together these results imply $x = y$.

When stated informally the assertions of most of these axioms seem obvious from an intuitive standpoint: [*P2*] each natural number has a natural number as a successor, and [*P5*] different numbers have different successors; [*P1*] there is at least one natural number 0 [$= \varnothing$], and [*P3*] it is not the successor of any number. It is only with axiom $P4$ that intuition falters slightly: no proper subset of the set of natural numbers can have 0 as a member and at the same time be such that if a number is in the subset, then so is its successor.

2 RECURSION THEOREM

Subsequently we shall have occasion to define a function on the set ω. Essentially this will be done by specifying the image at $\varnothing$ and then defining the value at x' in terms of the value at x.

What is needed is some assurance that such a function exists; this is given by the following theorem. The function g supplied by the theorem is said to be *defined by induction*.

Theorem 3   [*Recursion Theorem*]

Let c be a member of a set V and let f be a function from V into V. Then there exists a unique function g from ω into V such that $g(\varnothing) = c$ and $g(u') = f(g(u))$ for each u in ω.

Proof First let us show that such a function is unique if it exists. Suppose that g_1 and g_2 fulfill the conditions prescribed for g in the theorem. Let

$$A = \{u: \ u \in \omega \text{ and } g_1(u) = g_2(u)\}.$$

Clearly $\varnothing \in A$. If $u \in A$, then

$$g_1(u') = f(g_1(u)) = f(g_2(u)) = g_2(u')$$

so that $u' \in A$, and the uniqueness is established by *P4*.

Next we prove that such a function exists, and, since a function from ω into V is a subset of $\omega \times V$, we begin by considering such subsets. Let H be the collection of all subsets h of $\omega \times V$ such that

$$(\varnothing, c) \in h$$

and

$$(u,v) \in h \text{ implies } (u', f(v)) \in h.$$

Since $\omega \times V$ itself has these properties, it follows that H is not empty so that the intersection of its members is defined. Letting $g = \bigcap_{h \in H} h$, it is easy to see that $(\varnothing, c) \in g$. Also, if $(u,v) \in g$, then for each $h \in H$ it follows that $(u,v) \in h$ so that $(u', f(v)) \in h$, whence $(u', f(v)) \in g$. Thus g itself is a member of H.

In common with all members of H, the domain of g is ω. It remains only to prove that g is a function, for then it will have all the properties enunciated in the conclusion of the theorem. To do this, we consider the set B consisting of all members u of ω for which there is a unique $v \in V$ with $(u,v) \in g$; that is,

$$B = \{u: \ u \in \omega \text{ and } (u,v),(u,z) \in g \text{ imply } v = z\}.$$

We shall show that g is a function by establishing that B is an inductive set.

Suppose $\varnothing \notin B$. Since $(\varnothing, c) \in g$, it follows that there is some z with $c \neq z$ and $(\varnothing, z) \in g$. But then it is not difficult to verify that $g - \{(\varnothing, z)\}$ is a member of H, contrary to the fact that $g \subset h$ for all $h \in H$. We conclude that $\varnothing \in B$.

Next, suppose that there is some u with $u \in B$ and $u' \notin B$. Then, for some v, $(u, v) \in g$ so that $(u', f(v)) \in g$. Since $u' \notin B$, there is some z with $z \neq f(v)$ and $(u', z) \in g$. But then $g - \{(u', z)\}$ is a member of H, contrary to $g \subset h$ for all $h \in H$ ▲

Example To illustrate the recursion theorem, let us momentarily anticipate developments and suppose that the set of integers is available. To define the power function $g(n) = 2^n$ we might state that

$$g(0) = 1, \qquad g(n + 1) = 2 \cdot 2^n.$$

This amounts to an application of the recursion theorem in which V is the set of integers, $c = 1$, f is the function given by $f(x) = 2x$, and $n + 1$ is written for the successor of n.

EXERCISES AND EXTENSIONS

1. For each set A, let $f(A) = A \cup \{A\}$. By the recursion theorem, there is a function g with $g(\varnothing) = \omega$ and $g(u') = g(u) \cup \{g(u)\}$ for $u \in \omega$. Show that $\omega \cup \{g(u): u \in \omega\}$ is an inductive set.

2. Prove that if $x, y \in \omega$ and $x \neq y$, then $x' \neq y'$.

3. Prove that if $x \in \omega$, then $x' \neq x$.

4. Prove that if $x \in \omega$ and $x \neq \varnothing$, then there is a unique $z \in \omega$ such that $x = z'$.

5. Let f be a function defined on a set S and assume that:

S1. There is some s_0 that is a member of S.
S2. If $s \in S$, then $f(s) \in S$.
S3. If $s \in S$, then $f(s) \neq s_0$.

S4. If $B \subset S$, if $s_0 \in B$, and if $s \in B$ implies $f(s) \in B$, then $B = S$.

S5. If $s, t \in S$ and if $f(s) = f(t)$, then $s = t$.

Prove that $(\omega, ')$ and (S, f) are *isomorphic* systems in that there is a one-to-one mapping φ from ω onto S such that $\varphi(u') = f(\varphi(u))$ for each $u \in \omega$. Moreover, show that for such a mapping necessarily $\varphi(\varnothing) = s_0$.

6. Prove that the system (S, f) of Exercise 5 has the following property:

   S4'. If C is a nonempty subset of S, then there is some $s \in C$ such that $s \neq f(t)$ for all $t \in C$.

   Establish also that *S1*, *S2*, *S3*, *S4'*, and *S5* imply *S4*. [The property described in *S4'* is called the *well-ordering principle*. Applied to the set ω after an order has been defined, it asserts that a nonempty set of natural numbers has a least element. The present problem establishes that the well-ordering principle is equivalent to the principle of mathematical induction.]

7. (a) Let $S = \{s_0, s_1\}$ and let f be such that $f(s_0) = f(s_1) = s_1$. Verify that f and S satisfy *S1*, *S2*, *S3*, and *S4* of Exercise 5 but do not satisfy *S5*. This shows that *S5* is independent of *S1* through *S4*. (b) Produce additional examples to illustrate the independence of each of the remaining four axioms.

Natural Numbers

Chapter Three
Natural Numbers

1 INTRODUCTION

Hereafter we shall use only those properties of natural numbers that are described in the Peano axioms. No direct appeal will be made to the fact that natural numbers are sets of a certain character, and to emphasize this we shall adopt the convention of writing 0 for $\varnothing$. Throughout the chapter symbols such as x, y, s, and t denote any members of ω unless qualified to the contrary; for example, the statement "$x = y$" is understood to mean "$x, y \in \omega$ and $x = y$."

We note some immediate consequences of the Peano axioms. [Cf. Exercises 2 to 4 of Chapter 2.]

Theorem 1

$x \neq y$ implies $x' \neq y'$.

Proof Directly from $P5$ ▲

Theorem 2

$x' \neq x$.

Proof Let $A = \{x:\ x' \neq x\}$. Then $0 \in A$ by $P3$. Assume $x \in A$ so that $x' \neq x$. Then $(x')' \neq x'$ by Theorem 1; hence $x' \in A$ so that $A = \omega$ by $P4$ ▲

Theorem 3

If $x \neq 0$, then there is a unique z such that $x = z'$.

Proof If such a z exists, it is unique by $P5$. Let

$$A = \{0\} \cup \{x:\ \text{for some } z,\ x = z'\}$$

so that $0 \in A$ trivially. If $x \in A$, then $x' = z'$ for $z = x$ so that $x' \in A$. It follows that $A = \omega$ ▲

Before stating a formal definition of addition and multiplication, we shall illustrate the ideas that are involved. To begin with, for any natural number n it is clear that we should define $n + 0$ to be n. The successor of 0 will play the role of 1; for any n we shall take $n + 1$ to be the successor of n. Having defined sums such as these, we shall be able to use them to define all other sums. For example, to define the sum of 7 and 3 we start with $7 + 1 = 8$; then we take $7 + 2$ to be $8 + 1 = 9$; and we take $7 + 3$ to be $9 + 1 = 10$. More generally, to define the sum of 7 and any natural number n we assume that $7 + (n - 1)$ is defined and take

$$7 + n = [7 + (n - 1)] + 1.$$

This is, of course, an inductive definition and formally amounts to an application of the recursion theorem with $f(x) = x + 1$.

Once addition is defined and its properties established, we shall define multiplication as nothing more than repeated addition. For instance, we shall take $7 \cdot 0 = 0$, and, assuming that $7 \cdot (n - 1)$ is defined, we let

$$7 \cdot n = [7 \cdot (n - 1)] + 7.$$

Here the recursion theorem is employed with $f(x) = x + 7$.

2 ADDITION

Addition is defined on the set ω by using the recursion theorem. If in that theorem we let $V = \omega$, let $c = x$, and take f to be the function such that $f(y) = y'$ for all $y \in \omega$, then we conclude that there is a function g from ω into ω such that

(1) $$g(0) = x \quad \text{and} \quad g(y') = (g(y))'.$$

For any $y \in \omega$, let $x + y = g(y)$ and call this the *sum* of x and y. In this symbolism the equations of (1) become

(2)
$$x + 0 = x$$
$$x + y' = (x + y)'.$$

Since members of ω are equal if and only if they are identical, it follows that if $x = y$, then $x + z$ and $y + z$ are two symbols for the same member of ω so that $x + z = y + z$. We describe this by saying that in an addition equal quantities may be substituted for one another. This principle of substitution will be valid for all the operations that we shall consider and will be employed without further comment.

A sequence of theorems, most of which are proved by induction, establishes the basic properties of addition.

Theorem 4

$$0 + x = x \text{ and } y' + x = (y + x)'.$$

Proof Let A be the set of all $x \in \omega$ such that $0 + x = x$ and $y' + x = (y + x)'$ for all y in ω. Since $0 + 0 = 0$ and $y' + 0 = y' = (y + 0)'$ for all y, 0 is a member of A.

Assume that $x \in A$. Then $0 + x = x$ and $y' + x = (y + x)' = y + x'$. It follows that $0 + x' = (0 + x)' = x'$ and $y' + x' = (y' + x)' = (y + x')'$, implying that $x' \in A$ ▲

Corollary

$$y' + x = y + x'.$$

A proof such as the above is described as proof by *induction on x* to emphasize the special role played by that member. Similar proofs ordinarily will not be stated in such full detail; in particular, the counterpart of the set A will not always be defined explicitly.

Theorem 5 [*Commutative Law*]

$$x + y = y + x.$$

Proof The proof is by induction on x. The statement is true for $x = 0$ since $0 + y = y = y + 0$ by (2) and Theorem 4. Assume the *induction hypothesis*, that is, assume that the statement $x + y = y + x$ is valid for x. Then by these same results $x' + y = (x + y)' = (y + x)' = y + x'$ ▲

Theorem 6   [*Associative Law*]

$$x + (y + z) = (x + y) + z.$$

Proof   The proof is by induction on x.   Since $0 + (y + z) = y + z = (0 + y) + z$, the statement is true for 0.   Assume that $x + (y + z) = (x + y) + z$.   Then, by Theorem 4,

$$x' + (y + z) = [x + (y + z)]' = [(x + y) + z]'$$
$$= (x + y)' + z = (x' + y) + z \; ▲$$

Frequently we write simply $x + y + z$ for either of the sums appearing in the preceding theorem.   This is not ambiguous since the associative law ensures that the two possible interpretations of the symbol lead to the same result.   As associative laws are encountered in connection with other operations, similar conventions will be adopted; this will be done without further comment.

Theorem 7   [*Cancellation Law*]

$$x + z = y + z \text{ implies } x = y.$$

Proof   The statement obviously holds for $z = 0$; assume that $x + z = y + z$ implies $x = y$.   If $x + z' = y + z'$, then $(x + z)' = (y + z)'$ so that $x + z = y + z$ by $P5$; therefore $x = y$ from the induction hypothesis ▲

Corollary

$$x + z = x \text{ implies } z = 0.$$

Proof $x + z = x = x + 0$ so that $z = 0$ ▲

Theorem 8

$$x + y = 0 \text{ implies } x = y = 0.$$

Proof   For a change, the proof is not by induction.   Suppose that $x \neq 0$.   Then by Theorem 3 there is some z such that $x = z'$.   Hence $0 = x + y = z' + y = (z + y)'$, contrary to $P3$.   Thus $x = 0$, from which $0 = 0 + y = y$ ▲

The next theorem is somewhat different in character; we shall make extensive use of it in the chapter that follows.

Theorem 9

For any x and y there are unique numbers s and t such that $x + t = y + s$ and such that $s = 0$ or $t = 0$.

Proof   First we show that if such numbers exist, they are unique. Suppose that $x + t_1 = y + s_1$ with $s_1 = 0$ or $t_1 = 0$, and that $x + t_2 = y + s_2$ with $s_2 = 0$ or $t_2 = 0$.   Then

$$(3) \quad y + s_1 + t_2 = x + t_1 + t_2 = x + t_2 + t_1 = y + s_2 + t_1$$

so that, by the cancellation law,

$$(4) \qquad\qquad s_1 + t_2 = s_2 + t_1.$$

There are four cases to consider.   If $s_1 = s_2 = 0$, then $t_1 = t_2$ from (4).   Similarly, $t_1 = t_2 = 0$ implies $s_1 = s_2$.   If $s_1 = t_2 = 0$, then $s_2 + t_1 = 0$ so that $s_2 = t_1 = 0$ by Theorem 8 and, again, $s_1 = s_2$ and $t_1 = t_2$.   In the same way, $s_2 = t_1 = 0$ implies $s_1 = s_2$ and $t_1 = t_2$, completing the proof of uniqueness.

Next we prove that such numbers exist; to this end we let A be the set of all x such that the conclusion holds for all y in ω. Since $0 + y = y + 0$, it follows by taking $t = y$ and $s = 0$ that $0 \in A$.

Assume that $x \in A$.   Then for any y there exist s and t with $x + t = y + s$ and $s = 0$ or $t = 0$.   If $t = 0$, then $x = y + s$ so that $x' = (y + s)' = y + s'$.   If $t \neq 0$, then necessarily $s = 0$ so that $x + t = y$.   Also, there is some z such that $t = z'$; thus $x' + z = (x + z)' = x + z' = y$.   It follows from these two cases that $x' \in A$ whenever $x \in A$ ▲

3   MULTIPLICATION

Next we define a second operation on ω, called *multiplication*, and we develop rules for it similar to those of addition.   Let x be a member of ω.   In the recursion theorem, take $V = \omega$, $c = 0$, and let f be the function such that $f(y) = y + x$ for all $y \in \omega$. It follows that a function h exists from ω into ω with

(5) $\qquad h(0) = 0 \qquad$ and $\qquad h(y') = h(y) + x$

for all $y \in \omega$. If we write $x \cdot y$ or, simply, xy for $h(y)$, the statements of (5) become

(6) $\qquad\qquad \begin{aligned} x0 &= 0 \\ xy' &= xy + x \end{aligned}$

for all $y \in \omega$. The quantity xy is the *product* of x and y.

[In (6) we have followed convention by writing $xy + x$ for $(xy) + x$. Similarly, we shall write $xy + xz$ for $(xy) + (xz)$. Later in dealing with integers and real numbers, we shall employ similar conventions without further comment.]

Theorem 10

$$0x = 0 \text{ and } y'x = yx + x.$$

Proof The proof is by induction on x. It is easy to see that the statement is true for 0 since $z0 = 0$ for any z. If $0x = 0$, then, by (6), $0x' = 0x + 0 = 0$. Suppose that $y'x = yx + x$. From this, (6), and the corollary to Theorem 4,

$$y'x' = y'x + y' = yx + x + y' = yx + y + x' = yx' + x'.$$

It follows that the statement is true for x' if it is true for x ▲

Theorem 11 [Commutative Law]

$$xy = yx.$$

Proof By induction on x. First, $0y = 0 = y0$. Next, assume that $xy = yx$. Then $x'y = xy + y = yx + y = yx'$ ▲

Before proving that multiplication is associative, we establish the distributive law, which forms a bridge between addition and multiplication. This result is then used in the proof of associativity.

Theorem 12 [Distributive Law]

$$x(y + z) = xy + xz.$$

Proof The statement is true trivially for $x = 0$; assume that it is true for x. Then

$$x'(y + z) = x(y + z) + y + z = xy + xz + y + z = x'y + x'z \blacktriangle$$

Theorem 13 [*Associative Law*]

$$x(yz) = (xy)z.$$

Proof The statement is true trivially for $x = 0$; assume that it is true for x. Then

$$x'(yz) = x(yz) + yz = (xy)z + yz = (xy + y)z = (x'y)z \blacktriangle$$

Although the next result is an immediate consequence of (6), its fundamental role in multiplication is justification for including it among our list of theorems.

Theorem 14

$$x0' = x.$$

Proof $x0' = x0 + x = x \blacktriangle$

Finally, we prove two results for multiplication which are counterparts of earlier results for addition.

Theorem 15

$$xy = 0 \text{ implies } x = 0 \text{ or } y = 0.$$

Proof If $x \neq 0$, then by Theorem 3 there is some z such that $x = z'$. Thus $0 = xy = z'y = zy + y$, so that $y = 0$ by Theorem 8 $\blacktriangle$

Theorem 16 [*Cancellation Law*]

$$xz = yz \text{ and } z \neq 0 \text{ imply } x = y.$$

Proof By Theorem 9, there are numbers s and t such that $x + t = y + s$ and $s = 0$ or $t = 0$. Without loss of generality, let us suppose $t = 0$ so that $x = y + s$. Then $xz = (y + s)z = yz + sz$ and, from the hypothesis that $xz = yz$, we have $xz + 0 = xz + sz$. By the law of cancellation for addition, $0 = sz$ and, since $z \neq 0$, it follows from Theorem 15 that $s = 0$. But then $x = y$, as required ▲

This completes the list of properties that will be required in the construction of the system of integers, which is the subject of the next chapter.

EXERCISES AND EXTENSIONS

1.   Define $1 = 0'$, $2 = 1'$, $3 = 2'$, $4 = 3'$, $5 = 4'$, and $6 = 5'$. Prove (*a*) $2 + 3 = 5$, (*b*) $3 + 3 = 6$, (*c*) $3 \cdot 2 = 6$.

An *order* can be defined in the set of natural numbers as follows: For $x,y \in \omega$, we say that $x \leq y$ if and only if there is some $t \in \omega$ such that $x + t = y$.

2.   Show that the relation $\leq$ is a linear order in ω.

3.   Prove (*a*) if $x \leq y$, then $x + z \leq y + z$, and (*b*) if $x < y$, then $x + z < y + z$.

4.   Prove (*a*) if $x < y$, then $xz \leq yz$, and (*b*) if $x < y$ and $0 < z$, then $xz < yz$.

5.   Prove that (*a*) $x < x'$, and (*b*) $x < y$ if and only if $x' < y'$.

6.   (*a*) Establish that there is no y such that $0 < y < 0'$. [SUG-GESTION: Apply the least member principle to the set $A = \{y: \; 0 < y < 0'\}$.] (*b*) Establish that for all x there is no y such that $x < y < x'$.

A function f from ω into ω is said to be *order-preserving* if $x \leq y$ implies $f(x) \leq f(y)$.

7.   Prove that if f is order-preserving, then $x \leq f(x)$ for all $x \in \omega$.

8.   Let f be an order-preserving mapping from ω onto ω. Show that f is a one-to-one mapping.

The Integers

Chapter Four
The Integers

1 INTRODUCTION

With the natural numbers 0, 1, 2, . . . at our disposal we now turn to the development of the system of integers . . . , -2, -1, 0, 1, 2, ... Before we start the formal exposition, it will be well to take up the ideas behind the scene. The object here is to establish the existence of the integers and to describe all their properties by using only the properties of the nonnegative integers, i.e., the natural numbers. To begin with, we observe that each integer can be written in the form $x - y$ where x and y are non-negative; moreover, this representation is unique if we require that at least one of x and y must be zero. For instance, the integer -6 may be written $5 - 11$; but it can also be written $0 - 6$, and this is in the format that we desire. By writing (x,y) for $x - y$, we see that each integer may be regarded as a unique ordered pair of natural numbers; e.g., (0,2) is the integer -2, and (4,0) is 4.

To obtain sums and products of such ordered pairs, we merely perform the operations in the usual way and then reduce the results to the standard form. For example, from

$$[4 - 0] + [0 - 2] = 4 - 2 = 2 = 2 - 0$$

we see that (4,0) + (0,2) = (2,0). Similarly,

$$[4 - 0][0 - 2] = [4][-2] = -8 = 0 - 8$$

yields (4,0)(0,2) = (0,8). The technical difficulties involved in "reducing to standard form" are overcome by observing that

$$[x - y] + [u - v] = s - t$$

if and only if

$$x + u + t = y + v + s;$$

moreover, the values of s and t in this equation are unique if we stipulate that at least one of them is zero. From this it is clear that the pair (s,t) is the desired sum of (x,y) and (u,v). A similar calculation supports the definition of multiplication.

It is reasonable to say that an ordered pair (x,y) is nonnegative if $y = 0$. Once the nonnegative pairs have been identified, order can be introduced in the standard way; that is, $(x,y) \leq (u,v)$ if and only if $(u,v) - (x,y)$ is nonnegative.

2 ADDITION

Let I be the set of all ordered pairs (x,y) with $x,y \in \omega$ and $xy = 0$. [This last condition signifies only that $x = 0$ or $y = 0$.] An *integer* is a member of I. Our aim in this chapter is to introduce the basic operations and a linear order on the set of integers.

By Theorem 9 of Chapter 3, for given integers (x,y) and (u,v) there exist unique members s and t of ω such that $st = 0$ and

$$x + u + t = y + v + s.$$

Define the *sum* of (x,y) and (u,v) to be

(1) $$(x,y) + (u,v) = (s,t).$$

It is clear that (s,t) is a member of I, so that (1) defines an operation on I called *addition*.

As a special case of (1), if $y = v = 0$, then by taking $t = 0$ and $s = x + u$ in (1) it can be seen that

$$(x,0) + (u,0) = (x + u,\ 0).$$

The next several theorems establish fundamental properties of addition. Throughout the chapter the symbols (x,y), (u,v), and the like signify any members of I unless the contrary is stated.

Theorem 1 [*Commutative Law*]

$$(x,y) + (u,v) = (u,v) + (x,y).$$

Proof Let $(x,y) + (u,v) = (s,t)$ so that $x + u + t = y + v + s$. Then $u + x + t = v + y + s$ so that $(u,v) + (x,y) = (s,t)$, also ▲

Theorem 2

$$(x,y) + (0,0) = (x,y).$$

Proof   This follows from the fact that $x + 0 + y = y + 0 + x$ ▲

For members (x,y) and (u,v) of I to be equal it is necessary and sufficient that $x + v = y + u$.   The necessity of this condition is obvious, while the sufficiency is easily established by using Theorem 2.   Thus, if $x + v = y + u$, then $x + 0 + v = y + 0 + u$; hence $(x,y) + (0,0) = (u,v)$ from which $(x,y) = (u,v)$.

Theorem 3   [*Associative Law*]

$$(x,y) + [(u,v) + (w,z)] = [(x,y) + (u,v)] + (w,z).$$

Proof   Let $(u,v) + (w,z) = (s,t)$ so that

(2) $$u + w + t = v + z + s.$$

Also,   if $(p_1,q_1) = (x,y) + [(u,v) + (w,z)] = (x,y) + (s,t)$,   then $p_1 q_1 = 0$ and

(3) $$x + s + q_1 = y + t + p_1.$$

By adding (2) and (3) we obtain

$$(x + u + w) + q_1 + (s + t) = (y + v + z) + p_1 + (s + t)$$

from which

(4) $$(x + u + w) + q_1 = (y + v + z) + p_1$$

by use of the cancellation law.   Similarly, if $(p_2,q_2) = [(x,y) + (u,v)] + (w,z)$, then $p_2 q_2 = 0$ and

(5) $$(x + u + w) + q_2 = (y + v + z) + p_2.$$

Finally, by the uniqueness statement in Theorem 9 of Chapter 3, it follows from (4) and (5) that $p_1 = p_2$ and $q_1 = q_2$ ▲

Theorem 4

For any $(x,y) \in I$ there is some $(u,v) \in I$ such that $(x,y) + (u,v) = (0,0)$.

Proof Let (x,y) be given and take $u = y$ and $v = x$. The conclusion follows from the fact that $x + u + 0 = y + v + 0$ ▲

It is easy to see that the integer (u,v) of Theorem 4 is unique. For suppose that $(x,y) + (u,v) = (0,0)$ and $(x,y) + (z,w) = (0,0)$. Then

$$\begin{aligned}(u,v) &= (u,v) + (0,0)\\ &= (u,v) + (x,y) + (z,w)\\ &= (0,0) + (z,w)\\ &= (z,w).\end{aligned}$$

For any integer (x,y), we let $-(x,y)$ denote the unique integer such that $(x,y) + [-(x,y)] = (0,0)$, and we call $-(x,y)$ the *negative* of (x,y). The quantity $(x,y) + [-(z,w)]$ is denoted also by $(x,y) - (z,w)$ and is referred to as the *difference* of (x,y) and (z,w). In this way the operation called *subtraction* is introduced on I.

Further properties of addition can be established by appealing only to Theorems 1 through 4; the next result is in this category.

Theorem 5 *[Cancellation Law]*

If $(x,y) + (z,w) = (u,v) + (z,w)$, then $(x,y) = (u,v)$.

Proof Since (z,w) has a negative, it follows that

$$\begin{aligned}(x,y) &= (x,y) + (0,0)\\ &= [(x,y) + (z,w)] - (z,w)\\ &= [(u,v) + (z,w)] - (z,w)\\ &= (u,v) + (0,0)\\ &= (u,v) \text{ ▲}\end{aligned}$$

Corollary

If $(x,y) + (u,v) = (x,y)$, then $(u,v) = (0,0)$.

3 ORDER

A relation $\leq$ is defined in I by stating that $(x,y) \leq (u,v)$ if and only if there is some integer $(s,0)$ such that $(x,y) + (s,0) = (u,v)$.

Equivalently, $(x,y) \leq (u,v)$ if and only if there is some $s \in \omega$ such that $x + v + s = y + u$. Use of the symbol $\leq$ to denote the relation is justified by the following theorem.

Theorem 6

The relation $\leq$ is an order in I.

Proof The relation is reflexive because $(x,y) + (0,0) = (x,y)$ implies $(x,y) \leq (x,y)$. To establish antisymmetry, suppose that $(x,y) \leq (u,v)$ and $(u,v) \leq (x,y)$. Then, for some s_1 and s_2, $x + v + s_1 = y + u$ and $y + u + s_2 = x + v$. Combining these and using the cancellation law, we obtain $0 = s_1 + s_2$, so that $s_1 = s_2 = 0$ by Theorem 8 of Chapter 3. Hence $(x,y) = (u,v)$.

Finally, assume that $(x,y) \leq (u,v)$ and $(u,v) \leq (z,w)$. Then, for some s_1 and s_2, $x + v + s_1 = y + u$ and $u + w + s_2 = v + z$. From these it follows that $x + w + (s_1 + s_2) = y + z$ so that $(x,y) \leq (z,w)$. Thus the relation is transitive ▲

Theorem 7

The order $\leq$ is linear.

Proof For integers (x,y) and (u,v), there are natural numbers s and t such that $x + v + s = y + u + t$ and $st = 0$. If $t = 0$, then $(x,y) \leq (u,v)$; otherwise $s = 0$ and $(u,v) \leq (x,y)$ ▲

An integer (x,y) is *negative* if $(x,y) < (0,0)$ and *positive* if $(0,0) < (x,y)$. Since the order is linear, each integer can be classified uniquely as positive, negative, or zero. The following result provides a simple characterization of positive and negative integers.

Theorem 8

(x,y) is positive if and only if $x \neq 0$ and $y = 0$, and (x,y) is negative if and only if $x = 0$ and $y \neq 0$.

Proof We prove the first statement; the second is established in a similar manner. Suppose that (x,y) is positive so that

$$0 + y + s = 0 + x \quad \text{or} \quad y + s = x$$

for some $s \in \omega$. If $x = 0$, then $y = s = 0$ so that $(x,y) = (0,0)$, a contradiction. Hence $x \neq 0$; from this, $y = 0$ is automatic.

Conversely, let $(x,y) = (x,0)$ with $x \neq 0$. It follows from $0 + 0 + x = 0 + x$ that $(0,0) \leq (x,0)$. Equality is impossible with $x \neq 0$; hence (x,y) is positive ▲

From the fact that $0' \neq 0$ it can be seen that $(0,0) < (0',0)$. More generally, since $u' = u + 0'$ and $0' \neq 0$, it follows that $(u,0) < (u',0)$ and $(0,u') < (0,u)$. Incidentally, these statements provide formal recognition of the fact that the set I does not consist of just a single member.

Consider two nonnegative integers such that $(u,0) < (x,0)$. Then $u + s = x$ for some $s \in \omega$ with $s \neq 0$. It follows that $s = t'$ for some $t \in \omega$, and from this $u' + t = u + t' = x$; in other words, $(u',0) \leq (x,0)$. Thus $(u,0) < (x,0)$ implies $(u',0) \leq (x,0)$. In a similar fashion, $(0,y) < (0,v)$ implies $(0,y) \leq (0,v')$.

A property of order that tends to distinguish the integers from the real numbers to be constructed later is described in the next theorem. This testifies that under certain conditions a set must have a *least* member.

Theorem 9 [Least Member Law]

A nonempty subset of I that is bounded below has a minimum.

Proof Consider a nonempty subset C of I. We first establish the theorem in case C is bounded below by $(0,0)$; in this event members of C are of the form $(x,0)$.

Let A be the set of all $u \in \omega$ such that $(u,0)$ is a lower bound of C. From the nonempty character of C there is some $(x_1,0)$ in C, and, because $(x_1,0) < (x_1',0)$, it follows that $x_1' \notin A$; that is, $A \neq \omega$. Since 0 is obviously a member of A, we conclude that there must be some u_1 such that $u_1 \in A$ while $u_1' \notin A$.

Suppose that $(u_1,0)$ is not a member of C. Then, for each $(x,0) \in C$, $(u_1,0) < (x,0)$ so that $(u_1',0) \leq (x,0)$ by the remarks preceding this theorem. But this contradicts the fact that $u_1' \notin A$. We are forced to the conclusion that $(u_1,0)$ is a member of C and that, by virtue of its being a lower bound, it is the minimum of that set.

It remains to consider the case in which $(0,0)$ is not a lower bound of C, that is, the case of C having at least one negative member. Let B be the set of all $v \in \omega$ such that $(0,y) \leq (0,v)$ for some $(0,y) \in C$. Any lower bound of C must be a negative integer, and if $(0,z)$ is such a bound, it follows that $z' \notin B$. From this we conclude that $B \neq \omega$ and, since 0 is obviously in B, there exists some v_1 with $v_1 \in B$ and $v_1' \notin B$.

Because $v_1 \in B$, there is some $(0,y) \in C$ such that $(0,y) \leq (0,v_1)$. But the inequality cannot prevail, for if $(0,y) < (0,v_1)$, then $(0,y) \leq (0,v_1')$, contrary to the fact that $v_1' \notin B$. It follows that $(0,v_1)$ is a member of C and that it is the minimum of the set ▲

Turning to another aspect of order, we next show that it interacts with addition in a suitable manner.

Theorem 10

$(x,y) \leq (u,v)$ implies $(x,y) + (z,w) \leq (u,v) + (z,w)$.

Proof $(x,y) \leq (u,v)$ implies $(x,y) + (s,0) = (u,v)$ for some $(s,0) \in I$. From this $[(x,y) + (z,w)] + (s,0) = (u,v) + (z,w)$ so that $(x,y) + (z,w) \leq (u,v) + (z,w)$ ▲

4 MULTIPLICATION

The *product* of integers (x,y) and (u,v) is

$$(x,y)(u,v) = (xu + yv, \ xv + yu).$$

That the product is a member of I is easily verified by considering the various possibilities:

$$(x,0)(u,0) = (xu,0)$$
$$(x,0)(0,v) = (0,xv)$$
$$(0,y)(u,0) = (0,yu)$$
$$(0,y)(0,v) = (yv,0).$$

Thus an operation called *multiplication* is defined on I. The next several theorems express basic facts concerning multiplication; the proofs are routine.

Theorem 11 [*Commutative Law*]

$$(x,y)(u,v) = (u,v)(x,y).$$

Proof $(x,y)(u,v) = (xu + yv, \; xv + yu) = (ux + vy, \; uy + vx) = (u,v)(x,y)$ ▲

Theorem 12 [*Associative Law*]

$$(x,y)[(u,v)(z,w)] = [(x,y)(u,v)](z,w).$$

Proof

$$
\begin{aligned}
(x,y)[(u,v)(z,w)] &= (x,y)(uz + vw, \; uw + vz) \\
&= (xuz + xvw + yuw + yvz, \; xuw + xvz \\
&\qquad\qquad\qquad\qquad\qquad + yuz + yvw) \\
&= (xuz + yvz + xvw + yuw, \; xuw + yvw \\
&\qquad\qquad\qquad\qquad\qquad + xvz + yuz) \\
&= (xu + yv, \; xv + yu)(z,w) \\
&= [(x,y)(u,v)](z,w) \; ▲
\end{aligned}
$$

Theorem 13

$$(x,y)(0',0) = (x,y).$$

Proof $(x,y)(0',0) = (x0' + y0, \; x0 + y0') = (x,y)$ ▲

Theorem 14 [*Cancellation Law*]

$(x,y)(z,w) = (u,v)(z,w)$ and $(z,w) \neq (0,0)$ imply $(x,y) = (u,v).$

Proof From $(x,y)(z,w) = (u,v)(z,w)$ it follows that

$$(6) \qquad\qquad xz + yw = uz + vw$$

and

$$(7) \qquad\qquad xw + yz = uw + vz$$

and that at least one of these quantities is 0. Suppose that $xz + yw = uz + vw = 0$, from which $xz = yw = uz = vw = 0$. If $z \neq 0$, then $x = u = 0$; substitution of these values into (7) leads to $y = v$. If $w \neq 0$, then $y = v = 0$ and, again by (7), $x = u$. Since one of z and w is not zero, it follows that $x = u$ and $y = v$; that is, $(x,y) = (u,v)$. In a parallel manner, the assumption that $xw + yz = uw + vz = 0$ leads to the same conclusion ▲

The next theorem provides the connection between multiplication and addition; after that, we establish the link between multiplication and order.

Theorem 15   [*Distributive Law*]

$$(x,y)[(u,v) + (z,w)] = (x,y)(u,v) + (x,y)(z,w).$$

Proof   Let $(s_1,t_1) = (u,v) + (z,w)$ so that $s_1 t_1 = 0$ and

(8) $u + z + t_1 = v + w + s_1.$

It follows that

(9) $(x,y)[(u,v) + (z,w)] = (x,y)(s_1,t_1) = (xs_1 + yt_1, \; xt_1 + ys_1).$

Multiplying (8) by x and by y yields

(10)
$$xu + xz + xt_1 = xv + xw + xs_1$$
$$yu + yz + yt_1 = yv + yw + ys_1,$$

and by combining these we obtain a relationship between the coordinates of the integer of (9); thus

(11) $(xu + xz + yv + yw) + (xt_1 + ys_1)$
$$= (xv + xw + yu + yz) + (xs_1 + yt_1).$$

Turning to the other expression in the theorem, let

(12) $(s_2,t_2) = (x,y)(u,v) + (x,y)(z,w)$

so that $s_2 t_2 = 0$ and, by expanding (12),

(13) $(xu + yv + xz + yw) + t_2 = (xv + yu + xw + yz) + s_2.$

From (11), (13), and the uniqueness statement in Theorem 9 of Chapter 3,

(14) $xs_1 + yt_1 = s_2$ and $xt_1 + ys_1 = t_2.$

The distributive law follows from (9), (12), and (14) ▲

Theorem 16

$(x,y) \leq (u,v)$ and $(0,0) \leq (z,w)$ imply $(x,y)(z,w) \leq (u,v)(z,w)$.

Proof   Since $(x,y) \leq (u,v)$, there is some $(s,0) \in I$ such that $(x,y) + (s,0) = (u,v)$. The nonnegative character of (z,w) implies $w = 0$, so that

$$(u,v)(z,w) = (x,y)(z,w) + (s,0)(z,w) = (x,y)(z,w) + (sz,0) \;\blacktriangle$$

Starting at the beginning of the chapter with the *set* of integers, we have now arrived at a point where we have a *system* of integers; that is, besides the set of integers we have operations of addition and multiplication and an order relation that satisfy the various statements listed above.   From these basic statements can be derived those additional properties of integers that will be required, and we shall undertake this task in the next chapter.

The system of integers has been constructed in such a way as to have embedded within it a structure that is essentially the same as the natural numbers.   The mapping $\varphi(n) = (n,0)$ establishes a one-to-one correspondence from the set ω of natural numbers onto the set of nonnegative integers, and it is easily verified that, for all $m,n \in \omega$,

$$(15) \qquad \begin{aligned} \varphi(m + n) &= \varphi(m) + \varphi(n), \text{ and} \\ \varphi(mn) &= \varphi(m)\varphi(n). \end{aligned}$$

This is described by saying that the natural numbers and the nonnegative integers are *isomorphic*.   In effect, the nonnegative integers are a carbon copy of the natural numbers, and so the latter quantities can be dispensed with without essential loss.   Because of this, no formal reference to natural numbers will be made beyond this point.

EXERCISES AND EXTENSIONS

1.   Prove that (*a*) the sum and (*b*) the product of two positive integers is a positive integer.

2.   Establish that (x,y) is positive if and only if $-(x,y)$ is negative.

3. Verify the statements of (15) in Article 4.

4. Prove that the function φ from ω onto the set of nonnegative integers preserves order [where the order in ω is that defined in the Exercises and Extensions of Chapter 3].

Sometimes one encounters an alternative construction of the integers which is based on the set J of all ordered pairs (x,y) with $x,y \in \omega$ [the distinction between I and J being that the requirement $xy = 0$ is dropped]. In J, let $(x,y) \sim (u,v)$ if and only if $x + v = y + u$.

5. Prove that $\sim$ is an equivalence relation in J.

Addition is defined in J by letting $(x,y) + (u,v) = (x + u,\ y + v)$. This can be used to *induce* an addition in J^*, the collection of equivalence classes of J, as follows: If $A,B \in J^*$, if $(x,y) \in A$, and if $(u,v) \in B$, then $A + B$ is that member of J^* to which $(x,y) + (u,v)$ belongs.

6. Verify that the sum $A + B$ is unique, that is, it does not depend on the members or *representatives* of A and B chosen above.

7. Define *multiplication* in J by letting $(x,y)(u,v) = (xu + yv, xv + yu)$. Give an explicit statement of the corresponding operation induced in J^*. Show that the product in J^* does not depend on the representatives used to define it.

8. Assume the order in ω as defined in the Exercises and Extensions of Chapter 3. Give an explicit statement of the corresponding order induced in J^*; show that the order does not depend on the representatives involved in the definition.

9. Show that the system $(I, +, \cdot, \leq)$ is *isomorphic* with the system $(J^*, +, \cdot, \leq)$; that is, show that there is a one-to-one mapping from I onto J^* that preserves sums, products, and order.

Chapter Five

Properties of Integers

1 ORDERED GROUPS

The purpose of this chapter is to establish certain properties of integers that will be required in subsequent discussion. Since many of these laws apply equally well to other systems that will be encountered, it will be convenient to place some of our results in a more general setting, thereby avoiding a certain amount of repetition later on. We shall begin by considering implications of addition and order; later multiplication will be included in the discussion. In each instance, the customary symbol will be used for the operation or relation, so that it will not be necessary to repeat the name each time a symbol is introduced. Also, members of the various systems under discussion will be *equal* if and only if they are identical; it follows that the customary manipulations involving equality can be employed when need arises.

A *linearly ordered commutative group*, or simply an *ordered group*, is an ordered triple $(G, +, \leq)$ consisting of a set G, an operation $+$ defined on G, and a relation $\leq$ in G such that the following statements are true for any x, y, and z in G.

> *G1.* $x + y = y + x$.
> *G2.* $x + (y + z) = (x + y) + z$.
> *G3.* There is a *zero* θ of G such that $x + \theta = x$ for all $x \in G$.
> *G4.* Corresponding to x there is a *negative* $-x$ of G such that $x + (-x) = \theta$.
> *G5.* $\leq$ is a linear order in G.
> *G6.* $x \leq y$ implies $x + z \leq y + z$.

The following theorems concern any members x, y, and z of G. We begin by observing that the cancellation law for addition applies in this system.

Theorem 1

$x + z = y + z$ implies $x = y$.

Proof $x = x + \theta = (x + z) + (-z) = (y + z) + (-z) = y + \theta = y$ ▲

By using this theorem it is easy to show that θ is unique in possessing the property described in *G3*. For if we let θ_1 of G be such that $x + \theta_1 = x$ for some x, then $x + \theta_1 = x = x + \theta$; hence $\theta_1 = \theta$ from the theorem. Similarly, the negative of a member x of G is unique; for if $x + y = \theta$, then $x + y = x + (-x)$, from which $y = -x$. From this uniqueness we obtain certain rules for manipulating signs; as usual, $x - y$ signifies $x + (-y)$.

Theorem 2

$-(-x) = x$. Also, $-(x + y) = -x - y$ and $-(x - y) = -x + y$.

Proof Because $x + (-x) = \theta$ we may write $(-x) + x = \theta$ and observe that x is the negative of $-x$; that is, $x = -(-x)$. The second equation results from $x + y + (-x) + (-y) = x + (-x) + y + (-y) = \theta + \theta = \theta$. The third equation follows from the first two ▲

Closely related to the above results is the fact that certain linear equations always have solutions in this system.

Theorem 3

For $x, y \in G$ there is a unique member $z \in G$ such that $x + z = y$. Further, $z = y - x$.

Proof By direct substitution it is easy to see that $z = y - x$ satisfies the equation; thus,

$$x + z = x + y - x = y + x + (-x) = y + \theta = y.$$

Uniqueness of the solution follows from Theorem 1, for if $x + z_1 = y$ and $x + z_2 = y$, then $x + z_1 = x + z_2$ so that $z_1 = z_2$ ▲

Next we turn to some consequences of the order relation.

Theorem 4

$x < y$ if and only if $x + z < y + z$.

Proof $x < y$ implies $x + z \leq y + z$ by *G6*. But $x + z = y + z$ is impossible, for then $x = y$. Hence $x < y$ implies $x + z < y + z$. With this result, it follows from $x + z < y + z$ that $x + z + (-z) < y + z + (-z)$ or $x < y$ ▲

Corollary 1

$x \leq y$ if and only if $x + z \leq y + z$.

Corollary 2

$x < y$ if and only if $\theta < y - x$ if and only if $-y < -x$. Also, $x \leq y$ if and only if $\theta \leq y - x$ if and only if $-y \leq -x$.

As usual, a member x of G is *positive* if $x > \theta$ and *negative* if $x < \theta$. It is immediate from Corollary 2 that x is positive if and only if $-x$ is negative. Clearly a member of G is zero if and only if its negative is zero.

Theorem 5

$x \leq y$ and $z \leq w$ imply $x + z \leq y + w$.

Proof $x \leq y$ implies $x + z \leq y + z$, and $z \leq w$ implies $y + z \leq y + w$. Use of transitivity yields the desired result ▲

Theorem 6

$x \leq y$ and $y < z$ imply $x < z$. Also, $x < y$ and $y \leq z$ imply $x < z$.

Proof By *G5*, $x \leq y$ and $y < z$ imply $x \leq z$. But $x = z$ is impossible, for then $y < z = x$, contrary to $x \leq y$. Hence $x < z$. The second statement is proved in a like manner ▲

Theorem 7

$x \leq y$ and $\theta < z$ imply $x < y + z$.

Proof By Theorem 4, $y + \theta < y + z$, so that $x < y + z$ follows from Theorem 6 ▲

Corollary

$\theta < y$ and $\theta < z$ imply $\theta < y + z$.

The only other property of the system that we shall require is a relationship between the bounds of certain sets.

Theorem 8

Let A and B be subsets of G such that $x \in A$ if and only if $-x \in B$. Then a is an upper bound of A if and only if $-a$ is a lower bound of B. Further, $a = \max A$ if and only if $-a = \min B$, and $a = \sup A$ if and only if $-a = \inf B$.

Proof Assume that a is an upper bound of A. If $x \in B$, then $-x \in A$ so that $-x \leq a$, from which $-a \leq x$. It follows that $-a$ is a lower bound of B. If, in addition, a is the maximum of A, then $a \in A$ so that $-a$ is a member of B as well as a lower bound; hence it is the minimum of B. In the same way, a is an upper bound or a maximum of A if $-a$ is a lower bound or a minimum of B, respectively.

Suppose that a is the supremum of A. Then a is an upper bound so that $-a$ is a lower bound of B. Let b be any lower bound of B. Then $-b$ is an upper bound of A so that $a \leq -b$, from which $b \leq -a$. It follows that $-a$ is the infimum of B. The converse follows similarly ▲

2 ORDERED INTEGRAL DOMAINS

Next we bring multiplication into the system by turning to the investigation of an *ordered integral domain*. This is an ordered quadruple $(D, +, \cdot, \leq)$ consisting of a set D, operations $+$ and $\cdot$ on

D, and a relation $\leq$ in D; these must satisfy the following statements for any x, y, and z in D [where we write xy for $x \cdot y$].

D1. The ordered triple $(D, +, \leq)$ is a linearly ordered commutative group; that is, *G1* through *G6* are satisfied.

D2. $xy = yx$.

D3. $x(yz) = (xy)z$.

D4. There is a *unit* e of D such that $xe = x$ for all $x \in D$.

D5. $xz = yz$ and $z \neq \theta$ imply $x = y$.

D6. $x(y + z) = xy + xz$.

D7. $x \leq y$ and $\theta \leq z$ imply $xz \leq yz$.

D8. $\theta \neq e$.

Only one member of D has the property described in *D4*. For suppose that $xe_1 = x$ and $xe_2 = x$ for all $x \in D$. Then $e_2e_1 = e_2$ from the first equation and $e_1e_2 = e_1$ from the second. Hence $e_1 = e_1e_2 = e_2e_1 = e_2$.

In the theorems below we continue the convention that the variables involved designate any members of the system under discussion. We begin by examining the role of zero in multiplication.

Theorem 9

$x\theta = \theta$.

Proof $x = xe = x(e + \theta) = xe + x\theta = x + x\theta$ so that $x\theta = \theta$ from the uniqueness of θ ▲

Theorem 10

$xy = \theta$ implies $x = \theta$ or $y = \theta$.

Proof If $x \neq \theta$, then application of *D5*, the cancellation law for multiplication, to $xy = \theta = x\theta$ yields $y = \theta$ ▲

The results of Theorem 10 are described by saying that there are no *divisors of zero* in an ordered integral domain. The standard rules for manipulating "signs" are established next.

Theorem 11

$$(-x)y = x(-y) = -(xy).$$

Proof $xy + (-x)y = [x + (-x)]y = \theta y = \theta$ so that $(-x)y = -(xy)$ from the uniqueness of the negative. Similarly, $x(-y) = -(xy)$ ▲

Corollary

$$(-1)x = -x.$$

Theorem 12

$$(-x)(-y) = xy.$$

Proof $(-x)(-y) = (-x)(-y) + (-x)y + xy = (-x)[(-y) + y] + xy = xy$ ▲

These statements make it possible to perform all the usual manipulations involving negatives; for example, $x(y - z) = x[y + (-z)] = xy + x(-z) = xy + [-(xz)] = xy - xz$. Also, $-x(y - z) = x[-(y - z)] = x(-y + z) = x(z - y)$. We turn next to results involving order.

Theorem 13

Let z be positive. Then $x < y$ if and only if $xz < yz$.

Proof If $x < y$ and $\theta < z$, then $xz \leq yz$ by *D7*. But equality is impossible, for $xz = yz$ and $\theta < z$ imply $x = y$ by *D5*. Thus $xz < yz$. To prove the converse, assume that $xz < yz$ and consider the three possibilities: $x > y$, $x = y$, $x < y$. If $x > y$, then, by the first part of the proof, $xz > yz$, which is impossible. Since $x = y$ implies $xz = yz$, it too must be ruled out. We conclude that $xz < yz$ and $z > \theta$ imply $x < y$ ▲

Corollary 1

Let z be positive. Then $x \leq y$ if and only if $xz \leq yz$.

Corollary 2

$\theta < y$ and $\theta < z$ imply $\theta < yz$.

Theorem 14

$\theta < x < y$ and $\theta < z < w$ imply $xz < yw$.

Proof $x < y$ and $\theta < z$ imply $xz < yz$, and $z < w$ and $\theta < y$ imply $yz < yw$.   The result follows by applying Theorem 6 ▲

Theorem 15

$x < \theta$ and $y < \theta$ imply $\theta < xy$.

Proof $x < \theta$ and $y < \theta$ imply $\theta < -x$ and $\theta < -y$; hence $\theta < (-x)(-y) = xy$ ▲

Theorem 16

$x \neq \theta$ implies $\theta < xx$.

Proof   If $x > \theta$, then $xx > \theta$ by Corollary 2 to Theorem 13; if $x < \theta$, then $xx > \theta$ by Theorem 15 ▲

Corollary

$\theta < e$.   Further, $x < x + e$.

Proof   Since $\theta \neq e$ by *D8*, $\theta < ee = e$.   Then $x < x + e$ by Theorem 6 ▲

3   THE SYSTEM OF INTEGERS

With these preliminary investigations out of the way, let us return to the system of integers that was developed in Chapter 4. At this point it will be convenient to abandon the notation used earlier; henceforth we shall denote integers by symbols such as

m, n, p, etc. In keeping with this, we shall write simply 0 for the integer previously denoted by $(0,0)$ and write 1 for what was previously denoted by $(1,0)$. With these notational conventions, the various properties of integers that were proved in Chapter 4 are as follows:

I1. $m + n = n + m$.

I2. $m + (n + p) = (m + n) + p$.

I3. There is a *zero* 0 such that $m + 0 = m$ for all $m \in I$.

I4. Corresponding to m there is a *negative* $- m$ of I such that $m + (-m) = 0$.

I5. $mn = nm$.

I6. $m(np) = (mn)p$.

I7. There is a *unit* 1 of I such that $m1 = m$ for all $m \in I$.

I8. $mp = np$ and $p \neq 0$ imply $m = n$.

I9. $m(n + p) = mn + mp$.

I10. $\leq$ is a linear order in I.

I11. $m \leq n$ implies $m + p \leq n + p$.

I12. $m \leq n$ and $0 \leq p$ imply $mp \leq np$.

I13. $0 \neq 1$.

I14. Any nonempty subset of I that is bounded below has a minimum.

Examination of this list reveals that the system of integers is an ordered integral domain which, moreover, satisfies *I14*, the least member law. It follows that all the theorems of Articles 1 and 2 are valid for the integers; as is to be expected, the least member law will provide us with further useful results.

In subsequent discussion of the integers we shall use only those properties that appear in the above list or results, such as the theorems of this chapter, that can be derived from the above properties. No direct appeal will be made to the fact that the integers were constructed from the natural numbers in a certain way. For convenience, the symbol I will be used to designate the system of integers as well as the set of integers.

We turn now to some consequences of the least member law and note, first of all, that the dual statement is also true.

Theorem 17

Any nonempty subset of I that is bounded above has a maximum.

Proof   Let A be a nonempty subset of I that is bounded above and let $B = \{x: \ -x \in A\}$. Then B is nonempty, and it follows from Theorem 8 that B is bounded below. Hence B has a minimum by the least member law, and $-\min B$ is the maximum of A, also by Theorem 8 ▲

It was established in the corollary to Theorem 16 that n is less than $n + 1$; but without using the least member law, or something equivalent, it cannot be shown that there is no integer in between. We prove this next, one consequence being that it is then meaningful to describe $n + 1$ as the *next* integer after n.

Theorem 18

If $n > 0$, then $n \geq 1$.

Proof   Let $A = \{n: \ n \in I$ and $0 < n < 1\}$ and assume that A is not empty. Since the set is bounded below, it follows that A has a minimum; denote this by a. By definition, $0 < a$ and $a < 1$ from which $0 < aa$ and $aa < 1a = a < 1$. Hence aa is a member of A, contrary to the fact that a is the least member of the set. It follows that A is empty ▲

Corollary

$n < m$ implies $n + 1 \leq m$.

Proof   If $n < m < n + 1$, then $0 < m - n < 1$, a contradiction ▲

With these results, it can be shown that for any positive integer m the set I can be partitioned into disjoint sets $\{n: \ pm \leq n < (p + 1)m\}$, where $p \in I$.

Theorem 19

For $m,n \in I$ with $m > 0$, there exists a unique integer p such that $pm \le n < (p + 1)m$.

Proof First we establish uniqueness. If $pm \le n < (p + 1)m$ and $qm \le n < (q + 1)m$, then $pm < (q + 1)m$ and $qm < (p + 1)m$. It follows from Theorem 13 that $p < q + 1$ and $q < p + 1$ so that $p + 1 \le q + 1$ and $q + 1 \le p + 1$ by the corollary to Theorem 18. Thus p and q are equal, and we conclude that there can be at most one integer with the property described in the theorem.

To prove the existence of p, consider the nonempty set $A = \{pm: \ p \in I\}$. If this were bounded above, it would have a maximum $p_0 m$, contrary to the fact that $(p_0 + 1)m$ is in A. Thus A is not bounded above or, what is the same, $B = \{pm: \ p \in I$ and $pm > n\}$ is not empty. Since B is bounded below by n, it has a minimum $p_1 m$; clearly $(p_1 - 1)m \le n < p_1 m$ ▲

Corollary [Principle of Archimedes]

For $m,n \in I$ with $m > 0$, there is a positive integer q such that $n < qm$.

Proof If $n \le 0$, take $q = 1$. If $n > 0$, let $q = p + 1$, where p is the integer of the theorem. Then q is positive since qm and m are ▲

As was stated earlier, the set of nonnegative integers is essentially the same as the set of natural numbers. With little difficulty this relationship could be formalized and used to establish the following theorem, which is the *principle of mathematical induction* for integers. However, it is also a simple matter to prove the result by using the least member law, and we shall follow this course. By doing so we keep to the policy stated earlier of basing all properties of the integers on the fourteen statements listed at the beginning of this article.

Theorem 20

Let A be a subset of I such that $n_0 \in A$ and $n + 1 \in A$ if $n \in A$. Then $n \in A$ for all $n \ge n_0$.

Proof   Let $B = \{n: \ n \in I, \ n \geq n_0,$ and $n \notin A\}$ so that the set is bounded below by n_0; assume B to be not empty. Then B has a minimum b; and from $b \geq n_0$, $b \notin A$, and $n_0 \in A$, we conclude that $b > n_0$. Then $b - 1 \geq n_0$ and, since $b - 1$ is not a member of B, $b - 1 \in A$. However, from the property of the set A, it then follows that $(b - 1) + 1 = b$ is in A. From this contradiction we conclude B to be empty ▲

With the principle of induction established for I, it can now be seen that the recursion theorem is valid for the set of nonnegative integers. The result follows from the observation that this set satisfies the Peano axioms where, of course, $\varnothing$ is taken to be 0 and n' is taken to be $n + 1$. However, because it is meaningful to speak of one integer preceding another, it is now possible to state a generalization of the recursion theorem which amounts roughly to this: Instead of defining a function by specifying the value of $g(n + 1)$ in terms of $g(n)$, it is possible to specify $g(n + 1)$ in terms of the values $g(0), \ldots, g(n)$ at all of the nonnegative integers that precede $n + 1$. The new formulation includes the earlier theorem as a special case; at the same time it provides us with a certain flexibility that we shall require in the next article.

Before making a formal statement of this theorem, we introduce some new notation. Let I_ω be the set of nonnegative integers and, for each $n \in I_\omega$, let $I_n = \{m: \ m \in I$ and $0 \leq m \leq n\}$.

Let V be a nonempty set and let a member c of V be specified. Assume that there is a given function f that maps into V and whose domain is a set of functions; specifically, if, for any n, h is a function with domain I_n and range in V, then let $f(h)$ be a member of V. Since h is completely determined by its function values $h(1), \ldots, h(n)$, for the moment we also shall write $f(h(1), \ldots, h(n))$ for the function value $f(h)$; this will help to clarify the next comment.

It is desired to define a function g from I_ω into V which is such that $g(0) = c$ while $g(n + 1) = f(g(1), \ldots, g(n))$ for $n \in I_\omega$. Because the right member of the latter expression involves only the function values of g on the set I_n, it could just as well be expressed in terms of the function that is the restriction of g to the set I_n, which restriction we denote by $g|I_n$. Since the latter function is in the domain of f, the conditions on g may be expressed in the original notation as $g(0) = c$ and $g(n + 1) = f(g|I_n)$ for $n \in I_\omega$.

The proof of the following theorem differs from that of the earlier recursion theorem. In particular, the function g is defined as a union rather than an intersection. It is possible to employ this technique here because the domain of g is ordered; hence it is possible to refer to the *segments* I_n of the domain.

Theorem 21   [Generalized Recursion Theorem]

Let c be a member of a set V. Let f be a function such that if, for any $n \in I_\omega$, h is a function from I_n into V, then $f(h)$ is a member of V. Then there exists a unique function g from I_ω into V such that $g(0) = c$ and $g(n + 1) = f(g|I_n)$ for $n \in I_\omega$, where $g|I_n$ is the restriction of g to I_n.

Proof   Uniqueness is easy to establish. Suppose that g_1 and g satisfy the conclusion and that $g_1 \neq g_2$. Let m be the least member of I_ω for which $g_1(m) \neq g_2(m)$. Then $m > 0$ so that $m - 1 \geq 0$, and clearly $g_1|I_{m-1} = g_2|I_{m-2}$. Hence $g_1(m) = f(g_1|I_{m-1}) = f(g_2|I_{m-1}) = g_2(m)$, a contradiction.

The existence of g is established by considering functions much like g but whose domains are the sets I_n. Let H be the collection of all functions h such that, for some $n \in I_\omega$, h is from I_n into V, $h(0) = c$, and $h(m + 1) = f(h|I_m)$ for $0 \leq m < n$. Recalling that a function is a set, we first establish that if $h_1, h_2 \in H$, then $h_1 \subset h_2$ or $h_2 \subset h_1$; that is, h_1 is a restriction of h_2 or vice versa. Suppose that this is not the case, and let m be the least member of I_ω such that $h_1(m) \neq h_2(m)$. Then $m > 0$ and $h_1|I_{m-1} = h_2|I_{m-1}$, from which $h_1(m) = f(h_1|I_{m-1}) = f(h_2|I_{m-1}) = h_2(m)$, a contradiction.

Let $g = \bigcup_{h \in H} h$. Since each h is a collection of ordered pairs, so is g. If $h_1, h_2 \in H$ and if $(m,u) \in h_1$ and $(m,v) \in h_2$, then, by the last paragraph, both (m,u) and (m,v) are in h_1 or both are in h_2. Since h_1 and h_2 are functions, it follows that $u = v$; and from this we conclude that g is a function.

The domain of g must include 0, and $g(0)$ must equal c since the function $\{(0,c)\}$ is in H. Suppose that $n + 1$ is in dom g. Then, for some $h \in H$, $n + 1 \in$ dom h. Also, $h(m) = g(m)$ for

$m \in I_{n+1}$, from which it follows that $g(n + 1) = h(n + 1) = f(h|I_n) = f(g|I_n)$.

It remains only to prove that dom $g = I_\omega$. Assume that this is not the case, and let m be the least member of I_ω not in dom g. Then $m > 0$, and clearly I_{m-1} is contained in the domain of g. But it is easy to verify that the function $g|I_{m-1} \cup \{(m, f(g|I_{m-1}))\}$ with domain I_m is in H; hence $m \in$ dom g, a contradiction ▲

Corollary [*Recursion Theorem*]

Let c be a member of a set V and let f be a function from V into V. Then there exists a unique function g from I_ω into V such that $g(0) = c$ and $g(n + 1) = f(g(n))$ for each n in I_ω.

Proof Take the function of h in the theorem to be the mapping that assigns the image $f(h(n))$ to h ▲

The preceding theorem was established with the set I_ω as the domain of g. It is clear that the set of positive integers or, more generally, any set of the form $\{n: \ n \in I \text{ and } n \geq n_0\}$ would serve just as well.

4 GENERALIZED LAWS

The commutative, associative, and distributive laws can be generalized to cover more than two or three variables; we now turn our attention to this. Since the results to be obtained are valid beyond the system of integers, we assume once more that the elements under discussion are members of an ordered integral domain D. In fact, the order relation will play almost no role in the present article.

For any nonnegative integer n, we continue to denote the set $\{m: \ m \in I \text{ and } 0 \leq m \leq n\}$ by I_n. A function having domain I_n and range in D, an ordered integral domain, is called an *ordered* $(n + 1)$-*tuple* or an *ordered $(n + 1)$-tuple of members of D*. Such a function will usually be denoted by $(x_0, \ . \ . \ . \ , \ x_n)$, where, for

$0 \leq m \leq n$, x_m is the function value at m. Sometimes the symbols $(x_p, \ldots ,x_{p+n})$, $(x_0, \ldots ,x_{t-1},x_{t+1}, \ldots ,x_{n+1})$, and the like will be used for an ordered $(n + 1)$-tuple; the meanings of these should be clear. A *permutation* of I_n is a one-to-one mapping of I_n onto itself; such a function will be denoted by $(\pi(0), \ldots ,\pi(n))$.

The reader will recall that the symbol (x_0,x_1) for an ordered 2-tuple was used earlier for an ordered pair. It can easily be verified that this usage is unambiguous for, in an obvious way, each ordered pair determines a unique ordered 2-tuple, and conversely. Because of this, we can use the terms ordered pair and ordered 2-tuple interchangeably. Similar comments apply to ordered triples and quadruples.

With each ordered $(n + 1)$-tuple $(x_0, \ldots ,x_n)$ of members of D we associate a subset of D, each member of the subset being called a *sum* of $(x_0, \ldots ,x_n)$. We do this as follows. If $n = 0$, then a member u of D is a sum of (x_0) if $u = x_0$. If $n > 0$, then $u \in D$ is a sum of $(x_0, \ldots ,x_n)$ if there is some integer m with $0 \leq m < n$ such that $u = v + w$, where v is a sum of $(x_0, \ldots ,x_m)$ and w is a sum of $(x_{m+1}, \ldots ,x_n)$. From the generalized recursion theorem it follows that the notion of a sum is defined for every positive integer.

Remark The preceding definition involves an "informal" application of the generalized recursion theorem. Proceeding more literally, one might define the quantities appearing in that theorem as follows. Given D, let V be the collection of all functions φ such that, for some $n \in I_\omega$, dom φ consists of the set of all $(n + 1)$-tuples of members of D while ran φ is contained in the set of all subsets of D. Take c to be the function φ_0 with domain consisting of all 1-tuples and with $\varphi_0((x_0)) = \{x_0\}$. Let h be a function with domain $\{0, \ldots ,n\}$ and range in V, and write h_m for the function value of h at m for $0 \leq m \leq n$. Let $f(h)$ be that member of V whose domain is the set of all $(n + 2)$-tuples and which maps $(x_0, \ldots ,x_{n+1})$ onto a subset of D that is as follows. If there is some m such that $0 \leq m \leq n$ and for which dom h_m is not the set of all $(m + 1)$-tuples, then the subset of D is $\varnothing$; otherwise the subset of D is

$$\bigcup_{m \in I_n} \{v + w : \quad v \in h_m(x_0, \ldots , x_m) \text{ and}$$
$$w \in h_{n-m}(x_{m+1}, \ldots , x_{n+1})\}.$$

The resulting function g is such that, for each $n \in I_\omega$, $g(n)$ has domain consisting of all $(n + 1)$-tuples; and the image of $(x_0, \ldots , x_n)$ by the function $g(n)$ is a set, each member of which is a sum of $(x_0, \ldots , x_n)$.

A special case of a sum of $(x_0, \ldots , x_n)$, termed a *progressive sum*, is also defined inductively. Using the symbol $s(x_0, \ldots , x_n)$ for this sum, we take

$$s(x_0) = x_0$$

if $n = 0$, and

$$s(x_0, \ldots , x_n) = s(x_0, \ldots , x_{n-1}) + x_n$$

if $n > 0$. It can easily be seen that the progressive sum of $(x_0, \ldots , x_n)$ is a sum as defined above. Its usefulness stems from the following fact.

Theorem 22

Let m and n be nonnegative integers with $m < n$. Then for any $(x_0, \ldots , x_n)$

$$s(x_0, \ldots , x_m) + s(x_{m+1}, \ldots , x_n) = s(x_0, \ldots , x_n).$$

Proof   The proof will be by induction on n. The statement is vacuous for $n = 0$ and trivial for $n = 1$. Assume that it holds for n and let m be such that $0 \leq m < n + 1$. Consider the sum

$$s(x_0, \ldots , x_m) + s(x_{m+1}, \ldots , x_{n+1})$$

for two cases. If $m = n$, then $s(x_{m+1}, \ldots , x_{n+1}) = x_{n+1}$ and, from the definition of progressive sum,

$$s(x_0, \ldots , x_m) + s(x_{m+1}, \ldots , x_{n+1}) = s(x_0, \ldots , x_n) + x_{n+1}$$
$$= s(x_0, \ldots , x_{n+1}).$$

If $m \neq n$, the definition of progressive sum and the induction hypothesis may be used to obtain

$$s(x_0, \ldots ,x_m) + s(x_{m+1}, \ldots ,x_{n+1})$$
$$= s(x_0, \ldots ,x_m) + [s(x_{m+1}, \ldots ,x_n) + x_{n+1}]$$
$$= [s(x_0, \ldots ,x_m) + s(x_{m+1}, \ldots ,x_n)] + x_{n+1}$$
$$= s(x_0, \ldots ,x_n) + x_{n+1}$$
$$= s(x_0, \ldots ,x_{n+1}) \ \blacktriangle$$

The following theorem is the *generalized associative law of addition*. Roughly it states that, no matter how one groups the terms in an addition, they always add up to the same member of D.

Theorem 23

Any sum of $(x_0, \ldots ,x_n)$ is equal to $s(x_0, \ldots ,x_n)$.

Proof The proof is by induction on n. The statement is trivially true for $n = 0$. Assume it to be true for n, and let u be a sum of $(x_0, \ldots ,x_{n+1})$. Then for some m with $0 \leq m < n + 1$, $u = v + w$, where v is a sum of $(x_0, \ldots ,x_m)$ and w of $(x_{m+1}, \ldots ,x_{n+1})$. From the induction hypothesis and Theorem 22, it follows that

$$u = s(x_0, \ldots ,x_m) + s(x_{m+1}, \ldots ,x_{n+1})$$
$$= s(x_0, \ldots ,x_{n+1}) \ \blacktriangle$$

Since all sums of $(x_0, \ldots ,x_n)$ are equal, henceforth we shall use $x_0 + \cdots + x_n$ or $\sum\limits_{\nu=0}^{n} x_\nu$ to denote any one of them. By a trivial application of the induction theorem it can be seen that $\sum\limits_{\nu=0}^{n} x_\nu = 0$ if $x_\nu = 0$ for $0 \leq \nu \leq n$. The following results also follow easily.

Theorem 24

(a) $\displaystyle\sum_{\nu=0}^{m} x_\nu + \sum_{\nu=m+1}^{n} x_\nu = \sum_{\nu=0}^{n} x_\nu$ for $0 \leq m < n$.

(b) $\displaystyle\sum_{\nu=0}^{n} x_\nu + \sum_{\nu=0}^{n} y_\nu = \sum_{\nu=0}^{n} (x_\nu + y_\nu)$.

Proof   The first of these is essentially a restatement of Theorem 22. To establish the second, observe that it is trivial for $n = 0$; and if it holds for n, then

$$\sum_{\nu=0}^{n+1} x_\nu + \sum_{\nu=0}^{n+1} y_\nu = \left(\sum_{\nu=0}^{n} x_\nu + x_{n+1} \right) + \left(\sum_{\nu=0}^{n} y_\nu + y_{n+1} \right)$$

$$= \left(\sum_{\nu=0}^{n} x_\nu + \sum_{\nu=0}^{n} y_\nu \right) + (x_{n+1} + y_{n+1})$$

$$= \sum_{\nu=0}^{n} (x_\nu + y_\nu) + (x_{n+1} + y_{n+1})$$

$$= \sum_{\nu=0}^{n+1} (x_\nu + y_\nu) \blacktriangle$$

Another result, having to do with the rearrangement of the terms in an addition, is the *generalized commutative law of addition*.

Theorem 25

Let $(\pi(0), \ldots, \pi(n))$ be any permutation of I_n.   Then

$$\sum_{\nu=0}^{n} x_{\pi(\nu)} = \sum_{\nu=0}^{n} x_\nu.$$

Proof   The proof is by induction on n. Since the statement is obviously true for $n = 0$ [and $n = 1$], we assume it to be true for n and consider any permutation $(\pi(0), \ldots, \pi(n+1))$ of I_{n+1} and any $(n+2)$-tuple $(x_0, \ldots, x_{n+1})$. Then, for some $t, \pi(t) = n + 1$, so that

$$\sum_{\nu=0}^{n+1} x_{\pi(\nu)} = \sum_{\nu=0}^{t-1} x_{\pi(\nu)} + \sum_{\nu=t}^{n+1} x_{\pi(\nu)}$$

$$= \sum_{\nu=0}^{t-1} x_{\pi(\nu)} + x_{n+1} + \sum_{\nu=t+1}^{n+1} x_{\pi(\nu)}$$

$$= \sum_{\nu=0}^{t-1} x_{\pi(\nu)} + \sum_{\nu=t+1}^{n+1} x_{\pi(\nu)} + x_{n+1}.$$

Since $(\pi(0), \ldots, \pi(t-1), \pi(t+1), \ldots, \pi(n+1))$ is a permutation of I_n, it follows from the induction hypothesis that

$$\sum_{\nu=0}^{n+1} x_{\pi(\nu)} = \sum_{\nu=0}^{n} x_\nu + x_{n+1} = \sum_{\nu=0}^{n+1} x_\nu \blacktriangle$$

It is also a simple matter to establish the *generalized distributive law*.

Theorem 26

$$x \sum_{\nu=0}^{n} x_\nu = \sum_{\nu=0}^{n} xx_\nu.$$

Proof The statement is true trivially for $n = 0$; assume that it is true for n. Then

$$x \sum_{\nu=0}^{n+1} x_\nu = x \left[\sum_{\nu=0}^{n} x_\nu + x_{n+1} \right]$$

$$= x \sum_{\nu=0}^{n} x_\nu + xx_{n+1}$$

$$= \sum_{\nu=0}^{n} xx_\nu + xx_{n+1} = \sum_{\nu=0}^{n+1} xx_\nu \; \blacktriangle$$

In a completely analogous manner, one can define a *product* of an ordered $(n + 1)$-tuple of members of D and can prove *generalized associative and commutative laws for multiplication*. Here we confine our attention to the special instance of such products where the members of the $(n + 1)$-tuple are equal. This leads to the so-called *laws of exponents*.

For a nonnegative integer n and for any member x of D, define x^n, the nth *power* of x, inductively by

$$x^0 = e$$
$$x^{n+1} = x^n x \qquad \text{for } n > 0.$$

Theorem 27

Let m and n be nonnegative integers. Then for any x and y of D,

(a) $x^m x^n = x^{m+n}$,

(b) $(x^m)^n = x^{mn}$, and

(c) $(xy)^n = x^n y^n$.

Proof   It is easy to see that each statement is true for $n = 0$. Assume each is true for n.   Then $x^m x^{n+1} = x^m x^n x = x^{m+n} x = x^{m+n+1}$, which proves (a).   Next, $(x^m)^{n+1} = (x^m)^n x^m = x^{mn} x^m = x^{mn+m} = x^{m(n+1)}$, so that (b) is established.   Finally, $(xy)^{n+1} = (xy)^n (xy) = x^n y^n xy = x^n x y^n y = x^{n+1} y^{n+1}$ ▲

Various results follow easily for the order relation.   Typical of them are the following; we omit the simple inductive proofs.

Theorem 28

If $a > e$ and if n is a positive integer, then $a^n > e$.

Corollary

If $a > e$ and if n and m are integers such that $1 \leq m < n$, then $a^m < a^n$.

Theorem 29

If $x_\nu \leq y_\nu$ for $0 \leq \nu \leq n$, then $\displaystyle\sum_{\nu=0}^{n} x_\nu \leq \sum_{\nu=0}^{n} y_\nu$.

5   REPRESENTATION OF INTEGERS

We conclude the chapter by establishing further properties of the integers that will be required later.   One of them is the *Bernoulli inequality*.

Theorem 30

If m and n are nonnegative integers, then $(1 + m)^n \geq 1 + mn$.

Proof   This is true for $n = 0$; assume that it is true for n.   Then, since nm^2 is nonnegative,

$$(1 + m)^{n+1} = (1 + m)^n (1 + m) \geq (1 + mn)(1 + m)$$
$$\geq 1 + m(n + 1) + nm^2 \geq 1 + m(n + 1) \ \blacktriangle$$

Corollary

Let p and m be integers with $m \geq 1$. Then there is some positive integer n such that $p \leq (1 + m)^n$.

Proof By the principle of Archimedes there is a positive integer n such that $p < mn$, so that $p \leq (1 + m)^n$ by the theorem ▲

The remaining discussion concerns a way in which an integer can be represented to the base 10. It is much like the standard method of writing numbers, except that some of the leading digits are grouped together. To illustrate the general idea, observe that any integer can be represented in the form

$$a_0 10^2 + a_1 10 + a_2$$

where a_1 and a_2 are integers between 0 and 9 [note that a_0 is not subject to this restriction]. Thus we may write $(123)10^2 + (4)10 + (5)$ for the integer which is written 12345 in standard notation; also, $(0)10^2 + (1)10 + (2)$ is a way of writing 12. It is only with negative integers that the representation seems unusual; since a_1 and a_2 are nonnegative, the representation of $-246 = -300 + 54$ is $(-3)10^2 + (5)10 + (4)$.

This rather special representation of integers will be used in the next chapter to define addition and multiplication on the set of real numbers. The main result of the present article is contained in Theorem 33 and follows two preliminary theorems. The first of these is a generalization of the fact that $9 < 10$, $99 < 100$, etc; the second is used in establishing the uniqueness of the representation.

Theorem 31

If t and k are integers such that $0 \leq t < k$, then

$$9 \sum_{s=t+1}^{k} 10^{k-s} < 10^{k-t}.$$

Proof The statement is obviously true for $k = t + 1$; proceeding by induction, assume that it is true for k. It follows that

$$9 \sum_{s=t+1}^{k} 10^{k-s} \leq 10^{k-t} - 1.$$

Hence

$$9 \sum_{s=t+1}^{k+1} 10^{k+1-s} = 9 \left[1 + 10 \sum_{s=t+1}^{k} 10^{k-s} \right]$$

$$\leq 9 + 10(10^{k-t} - 1) < 10^{k+1-t} \blacktriangle$$

Theorem 32

Let $(c_0, \ldots, c_k)$ be a $(k+1)$-tuple of members of I such that $-9 \leq c_s \leq 9$ for $1 \leq s \leq k$. Then $0 < \sum_{s=0}^{k} c_s 10^{k-s}$ if and only if there is some integer m with $0 \leq m \leq k$ such that $c_m > 0$ and $c_n = 0$ for $0 \leq n < m$.

Proof For any integer m with $0 \leq m \leq k$,

$$\sum_{s=m}^{k} c_s 10^{k-s} = c_m 10^{k-m} + \sum_{s=m+1}^{k} c_s 10^{k-s}.$$

From Theorem 31 and the restriction on the quantities c_s it follows that

$$-10^{k-m} < -9 \sum_{s=m+1}^{k} 10^{k-s} \leq \sum_{s=m+1}^{k} c_s 10^{k-s}$$

$$\leq 9 \sum_{s=m+1}^{k} 10^{k-s} < 10^{k-m}$$

so that

$$(1) \qquad (c_m - 1)10^{k-m} < \sum_{s=m}^{k} c_s 10^{k-s} < (c_m + 1)10^{k-m}.$$

Assume $\sum_{s=0}^{k} c_s 10^{k-s}$ is positive. Then it is not possible to have $c_s = 0$ for all s satisfying $0 \leq s \leq k$; hence there is some least integer m with $0 \leq m \leq k$ and $c_m \neq 0$. Thus $c_n = 0$ for $0 \leq n < m$ and

$$(2) \qquad \sum_{s=0}^{k} c_s 10^{k-s} = \sum_{s=m}^{k} c_s 10^{k-s}.$$

Since this quantity is positive, it follows from (1) that $0 < c_m + 1$ or $0 \leq c_m$. But $c_m \neq 0$ so that $c_m > 0$, and this proves the theorem in one direction.

Next, assume m exists with $c_m > 0$ and $c_n = 0$ for $0 \leq n < m$. Then (2) is valid; since $c_m - 1 \geq 0$, it follows from (1) that the sum in (2) is positive ▲

Theorem 33

For any integer a there exists a unique $(k + 1)$-tuple $(a_0, \ldots ,a_k)$ of members of I such that $0 \leq a_s \leq 9$ for $1 \leq s \leq k$ and

$$a = \sum_{s=0}^{k} a_s 10^{k-s}.$$

Proof To see that such a representation is unique, suppose that

$$a = \sum_{s=0}^{k} a_s 10^{k-s} = \sum_{s=0}^{k} b_s 10^{k-s},$$

and let m be the least integer for which $a_m \neq b_m$. If $c_s = a_s - b_s$ for $0 \leq s \leq k$, it follows that $-9 \leq c_s \leq 9$ for $1 \leq s \leq k$ and that $c_m \neq 0$ and $c_n = 0$ for $0 \leq n < m$; also

$$\sum_{s=0}^{k} c_s 10^{k-s} = 0.$$

But this is a contradiction to Theorem 32.   Hence the representation of the theorem is unique if it exists.

Existence is established by induction on k.   There is no problem with $k = 0$; hence we assume the statement is true for k and turn our attention to $k + 1$.   For a given integer a, there is, by Theorem 19, an integer a_0 such that

$$a_0 10^{k+1} \leq a < (a_0 + 1)10^{k+1}.$$

Let $b = a - a_0 10^{k+1}$, then

$$(3) \qquad\qquad 0 \leq b < 10^{k+1}.$$

By the induction hypothesis, $(b_0, \ldots ,b_k)$ exists with $0 \leq b_s \leq 9$ for $1 \leq s \leq k$ such that

$$b = \sum_{s=0}^{k} b_s 10^{k-s} = b_0 10^k + \sum_{s=1}^{k} b_s 10^{k-s},$$

and from Theorem 31

(4) $$b_0 10^k \leq b < (b_0 + 1)10^k.$$

Combining (3) and (4) we obtain

$$0 \leq b < (b_0 + 1)10^k \quad \text{and} \quad b_0 10^k \leq b < 10^{k+1}$$

from which we conclude $0 \leq b_0 \leq 9$. By letting $a_s = b_{s-1}$ for $1 \leq s \leq k + 1$, it follows that $0 \leq a_s \leq 9$ for $1 \leq s \leq k + 1$ and

$$a = \sum_{s=0}^{k+1} a_s 10^{k+1-s} \quad \blacktriangle$$

EXERCISES AND EXTENSIONS

1. Prove that in an ordered integral domain there is no member x such that $x^2 + e = \theta$.

2. Show that in an ordered integral domain the cancellation law of multiplication [*D5*] can be derived from other assumptions.

Two ordered integral domains D and D' are *isomorphic* if there is a one-to-one mapping φ of D onto D' such that, for $x,y \in D$, $\varphi(x + y) = \varphi(x) + \varphi(y)$, $\varphi(xy) = \varphi(x)\varphi(y)$, and $x \leq y$ if and only if $\varphi(x) \leq \varphi(y)$. The mapping φ is called an *isomorphism* or an *isomorphic mapping*.

3. Prove that in such an isomorphism (*a*) the zero elements of D and D' correspond, (*b*) the units of D and D' correspond, and (*c*) $\varphi(-x) = -\varphi(x)$ for $x \in D$.

4. Prove that any ordered integral domain D' contains a subdomain that is isomorphic to I, the system of integers. [SUG-GESTION: Let $\varphi(0) = \theta'$ and let $\varphi(n + 1) = \varphi(n) + e'$ for $n \geq 0$, where θ' and e' are the zero and unit of D', respectively. For $n < 0$, let $\varphi(n) = -\varphi(-n)$.]

5. Prove that any ordered integral domain D' which satisfies the least member principle [*I14*] is isomorphic to I. [SUG-

GESTION: Use the isomorphism of Exercise 4; assume φ is not onto D'; show there must then be a least positive member c' that is not in the range of φ; use this to arrive at a contradiction.]

6. Give a proof of the recursion theorem that is analogous to the proof of the generalized recursion theorem; that is, give a proof in which the function g is defined as a union rather than an intersection.

7. Prove (*a*) the generalized associative and (*b*) the generalized commutative law for multiplication.

8. For each specified a and k, determine the $(k + 1)$-tuple $(a_0, \ldots , a_k)$ as described in Theorem 33: (*a*) $a = 12345$, $k = 2$; (*b*) $a = 12345$, $k = 3$; (*c*) $a = -12345$, $k = 2$; (*d*) $a = -29$, $k = 2$.

For each $n \in I_\omega$ let $I_n = \{m: \ m \in I \text{ and } 0 \leq m \leq n\}$. A set A is *finite* if A is empty or is equivalent to I_n for some $n \in I_\omega$; otherwise A is *infinite*.

9. (*a*) Prove, by induction on n, that if B is a proper subset of I_n, then $B \sim I_m$ for some $m < n$ or B is empty. (*b*) Conclude from this that any subset of a finite set is finite; also, that a set containing an infinite set is infinite.

10. (*a*) Prove that I_n is not equivalent to a proper subset of itself. (*b*) Conclude from this that a set that is equivalent to a proper subset of itself is infinite.

11. Prove that if I_m is equivalent to a subset of I_n, then $m \leq n$.

12. Show that I_ω is equivalent to a proper subset of itself, hence that it is infinite.

13. Prove that if A and B are finite, then so is $A \cup B$. [SUG-GESTION: First assume that A and B are disjoint; deal with the general case by using the fact that $A \cup B = A \cup (B - A)$.]

A set is *countably infinite* if it is equivalent to I_ω.
A set is *countable* if it is finite or is countably infinite; otherwise it is *noncountable*.

14. Verify that a countably infinite set is infinite.

15. Prove that a set is countable if and only if it is equivalent to a subset of I_ω.

16. Prove that a set is noncountable if it contains a noncountable subset.

17. Establish that the union of a countably infinite collection of countably infinite sets is countably infinite. [SUGGESTION: For $m = 1, 2, \ldots$, let the members of the mth set be denoted by a_{mn}, $n = 1, 2, \ldots$. Set up a correspondence with I_ω by considering the path

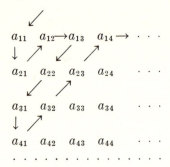

In some way, deal with the fact that the sets may not be disjoint.]

18. Prove that the union of a countable collection of countable sets is countable.

19. Prove that the collection of all ordered pairs (m,n) with $m,n \in I$ is countable.

20. Establish that the set of all finite subsets of I_ω is countable.

21. Prove that the set of all functions each having domain I_ω and range in I_1 is noncountable. [SUGGESTION: Assume that the collection F of all such functions is countable; hence that $F = \{f_n: \ n = 0,1, \ldots\}$. Define g on I_ω by letting $g(n) = 0$

if $f_n(n) = 1$ and $g(n) = 1$ if $f_n(n) = 0$. Show that $g \in F$, yet $g \neq f_n$ for all n. From this contradiction conclude that F is noncountable. This is known as the *Cantor diagonal proof* and is the main technique for establishing noncountability of sets.]

22. Prove that the set of all subsets of I_ω is noncountable. [SUG-GESTION: The *characteristic function* f_A of a subset A of I_ω is defined by $f_A(n) = 1$ if $n \in A$, $f_A(n) = 0$ if $n \notin A$. Establish an equivalence between the collection of subsets and the collection of characteristic functions; apply the results of Exercise 21.]

The *axiom of choice* is the assertion that if $\mathcal{C}$ is a nonempty collection of nonempty sets, then there exists a function c with domain $\mathcal{C}$ such that $c(A) \in A$ for each $A \in \mathcal{C}$. The function c is called a *choice function* since it makes a "choice" of one member from each of the sets of $\mathcal{C}$; in this language the axiom asserts that such a simultaneous choice of one member from each of several sets can always be made. Although the axiom of choice has strong intuitive appeal, it was established in 1963 by P. J. Cohen that this axiom is logically independent of the axioms of set theory.

23. Prove that the following assertion is equivalent to the axiom of choice: Every relation contains a function with the same domain.

24. Prove that an infinite set contains a countably infinite subset. [SUGGESTION: Let V be the collection of finite subsets of an infinite set X. Then there is a choice function c such that $c(X - A) \in X - A$ for $A \in V$. Define f on V by $f(A) = A \cup \{c(X - A)\}$, and let g be defined recursively from I_ω into V by $g(0) = \varnothing$ and $g(n + 1) = f(g(n))$. Finally, take $v(n) = c(X - g(n))$ and establish that (a) $v(n) \notin g(n)$, (b) $v(n) \in g(n + 1)$, (c) $g(n) \subset g(m)$ if $n \leq m$, and (d) $v(n) \neq v(m)$

if $n < m$. This proves that v is the required one-to-one mapping.]

25. According to Dedekind, a set is *infinite* if and only if it can be placed in one-to-one correspondence with a proper subset of itself. Establish that this is equivalent to the definition of infinity given above. [SUGGESTION: To establish that such a correspondence is possible, let $A = \{x_n: \ n \in I_\omega\}$ be a countably infinite subset of the infinite set X. Define h on X by $h(x) = x$ if $x \in X - A$ and $h(x_n) = x_{n+1}$ if $x \in A$ and $x = x_n$.]

An integer c is *divisible* by an integer b and we write $b|c$ if there is an integer d such that $c = bd$. If this is the case, we say that c is a *multiple* of b and that b is a *factor* of c.

26. Show that the relation $b|c$ of divisibility is (*a*) reflexive and (*b*) transitive.

27. Prove that (*a*) if $a|b$ and $a|c$, then $a|(b + c)$ and (*b*) if $a|b$, $a > 0$, and $b > 0$, then $a \leq b$.

28. Prove that the only divisors of 1 are 1 and -1. This means that 1 and -1 are the only integers that have inverses.

29. For a given nonzero integer m, define a relation R in I by saying that $a \, R \, b$ if and only if $b - a$ is divisible by m. Prove that R is an equivalence relation. [R is called a *congruence* relation, and $a \equiv b(m)$ is generally written for $a \, R \, b$.]

30. [*Division Algorithm*] (*a*) Prove that for integers a and b, with $b > 0$, there exist integers q [the *quotient*] and r [the *remainder*] such that $a = bq + r$ and $0 \leq r < b$. [SUGGESTION: Show that the set $\{a - bx: \ x \in I, \ a - bx \geq 0\}$ is not empty, hence has a least member $a - bq = r$. Verify that $0 \leq r < b$.] (*b*) Prove that q and r of part (*a*) are unique.

31. An integer a is *even* if $a = 2b$ and is *odd* if $a = 2b + 1$ for some integer b. Use the division algorithm to prove that each integer is even or odd, but not both.

32. (*a*) Prove that an integer *a* is even if and only if a^2 is even.
(*b*) Prove that there is no integer *a* such that $a^2 = 2$.

An integer *a* is a *common divisor* of *b* and *c* in case $a|b$ and $a|c$. If at least one of *b* and *c* is not zero, the set of common divisors of *b* and *c* is finite; the largest among the common divisors is called the *greatest common divisor* of *b* and *c*, and it is denoted by (b,c).

33. Prove that if $b \neq 0$ or $c \neq 0$, then there exist integers *s* and *t* such that $(b,c) = sb + tc$. [SUGGESTION: Show that $\{sb + tc: s,t \in I,\ sb + tc > 0\}$ is not empty, hence has a least member *d*. By contradiction, prove that $d|b$ and $d|c$. Next show that $(b,c)|d$, and conclude that $d = (b,c)$.]

34. Prove that if $c|ab$ and if $(b,c) = 1$, then $c|a$.

An integer $p > 1$ is called a *prime* if it has no divisor *d* such that $1 < d < p$.

35. Prove that the set of prime numbers is infinite. [SUGGESTION: If $p_1, \ldots, p_n$ are primes, then none of them divides $p_1 p_2 \cdots p_n + 1$.]

36. If *p* is prime and $p|ab$, then $p|a$ or $p|b$.

37. [*Fundamental Theorem of Arithmetic*] (*a*) Any integer exceeding 1 can be expressed as a product of primes. [SUGGESTION: By induction establish the proposition $P(n)$ that any integer *a* such that $1 \leq a \leq n$ can be so expressed.] (*b*) Apart from order of the factors, the prime factorization of part (*a*) is unique. [SUGGESTION: Assume two such factorizations; apply Exercise 36 to prove that they agree.]

The Real Numbers

Chapter Six
The Real Numbers

1 INTRODUCTION

We are now in a position to develop the system of real numbers, and there are several ways in which this can be done. One general approach is first to define the so-called *system of rational numbers*. This is usually done by considering the set of all ordered pairs of integers; by introducing appropriate definitions of addition, multiplication, and order; and by defining a rational number to be a certain equivalence class in the system so constructed. There are two standard methods for constructing real numbers from the system of rational numbers. Following Dedekind, one may consider the collection of *Dedekind cuts*, each member of which is a subset of the set of rational numbers. These cuts, or subsets, must satisfy certain conditions, the essential one being that each member of a cut must be greater than all rational numbers that are not in the cut. Addition, multiplication, and order are introduced on the set of cuts; the result is the system of real numbers. While the notion of a cut is sometimes not easy to grasp on an intuitive basis, the Dedekind method results in a very elegant mathematical structure and is of historical importance as being the first satisfactory definition of a real number.

Another definition of real number, due to Cantor, is based on certain sequences. One considers the collection of all sequences $\{x_n\}$ of rational numbers that satisfy the *Cauchy condition:* For any rational number $\varepsilon > 0$ there is an integer N such that $|x_p - x_q| < \varepsilon$ for all integers p and q exceeding N. Addition, multiplication, and order are introduced, and two sequences are said to be equivalent if their difference converges to zero. The resulting collection of equivalence classes is the set of real numbers. The appeal of Cantor's definition stems in no small way from the fact that it can be generalized easily to other mathematical settings.

The Dedekind and Cantor definitions are discussed in much

greater detail in the last two chapters of this book. The definition of real number given in this chapter is yet another. Since it is based directly on the system of integers, it will be unnecessary to engage in a preliminary discussion of the rational number system.

The usual way of visualizing real numbers is in terms of their representation to the base 10; that is, one tends to think of them as entities such as 12.5 and 3.14159 $\cdots$. These can be viewed as sequences $a_0 \cdot a_1a_2a_3 \cdots$ of integers, where the first integer is arbitrary and all after the first lie between 0 and 9; it is this view that motivates the definition which we are about to present. One technical difficulty that arises with this notion of a real number is that the decimal representation of a real number is not unique; for instance, the number 1 may also be written 0.9999 $\cdots$. To surmount this, in what follows we shall simply exclude those sequences that terminate in nines.

The ensuing articles develop the system of real numbers in a formal way; before turning to this, let us discuss informally what we are about to do. At this stage we have only the integers at our disposal, and so we must develop all properties of real numbers by referring only to properties of integers. For instance, to see that the real number 13.754 is less than 13.76, we observe that the leading integers are equal as are the first decimals, but the integer 5 is less than the integer 6 in the second decimal place. More generally, the relative order of any two real numbers can be established by comparing their decimal representations digit by digit; since this comparison is one of integers, the order properties of integers can be used to induce an order on the real numbers.

Addition and multiplication of real numbers present no problems provided the numbers involved have decimal expansions that terminate in zeros. This can be done simply by "shifting the decimal." To illustrate, suppose we wish to determine the sum of 12.5 and 4.796. Since we can discuss addition only of integers, we shift the decimal three places, find that

$$12500 + 4796 = 17296,$$

shift the decimal back, and quote the answer as 17.296. For the product, we find that

$$(12500)(4796) = 59950000;$$

this time we shift the decimal back six places and quote the answer as 59.95. Note carefully that all calculations here take place in the system of integers.

One technical problem must be considered: What would happen if we were to shift the decimal further and use, say, 125000 and 47960 in the above calculations? It is easy to verify that the results obtained would be the same provided the decimal is positioned properly, which means a shift back by the original amount in the addition, and by double that amount in the multiplication.

The "shifting" back and forth that we have been discussing is accomplished formally by mapping the real numbers into the set of integers. There are different mappings corresponding to the varying amounts of shift; these are introduced later and are called k-mappings.

The numbers with decimal expansion terminating in zeros form a dense subset of the set of real numbers. Once addition and multiplication have been defined on the dense subset, the operations can be extended to all real numbers by what are essentially limiting procedures. To illustrate this for addition, suppose we wish to add $\frac{1}{9} = 0.1111 \cdots$ and $\pi = 3.14159 \cdots$. We may consider a sequence of approximations obtained by truncating the decimals of $\frac{1}{9}$ and π, and adding; thus,

$$
\begin{aligned}
0 &\quad + 3 &&= 3 \\
0.1 &\quad + 3.1 &&= 3.2 \\
0.11 &\quad + 3.14 &&= 3.25 \\
0.111 &\quad + 3.141 &&= 3.252
\end{aligned}
$$

$\cdot \ \cdot \ \cdot \ \cdot \ \cdot \ \cdot \ \cdot \ \cdot \ \cdot \ \cdot \ \cdot \ \cdot \ \cdot \ \cdot$

Note that sums of real numbers such as these can be computed, since they terminate in zeros. The sequence 3, 3.2, 3.25, 3.252, . . . of sums is increasing and has a supremum which we take to be the sum of $\frac{1}{9}$ and π. A similar technique is used to extend multiplication to the full set of real numbers.

2 ORDER

Let us now begin the formal development of the real number system. We continue the convention that I denotes both the set and the system of integers; as before, I_ω signifies the set of all non-negative integers, and $I_9 = \{n:\ n \in I,\ 0 \le n \le 9\}$. Let $\mathfrak{R}$ be the collection of all functions f such that

(1)
- (a) f is from I_ω into I,
- (b) $f(n) \in I_9$ if $n \ge 1$, and
- (c) For any $m \in I_\omega$ there is some $n \in I_\omega$ with $n > m$ and $f(n) \ne 9$.

A *real number* is defined to be a member of $\mathfrak{R}$.

Example 1 A member of $\mathfrak{R}$ may be denoted by $(x_0, x_1, x_2, \ldots)$, where x_n is the function value at n for $n \in I_\omega$. Thus $(12,1,1,1, \ldots)$ and $(-4,2,3,0,0, \ldots)$ are members of $\mathfrak{R}$. It will evolve that these are, respectively, the real numbers customarily written $12.11 \cdots = 12\frac{1}{9}$ and $-4 + 0.23 = -3.77$.

Special symbols will be reserved for certain members of $\mathfrak{R}$. Thus θ, called *zero*, is that member of $\mathfrak{R}$ such that $\theta(n) = 0$ for all n in I_ω. The function e of $\mathfrak{R}$ satisfying $e(0) = 1$ and $e(n) = 0$ for $n \ge 1$ is called the *unit*. Moreover, for any $p \in I_\omega$, we reserve the symbol e^p for that member of $\mathfrak{R}$ such that $e^p(p) = 1$ and $e^p(n) = 0$ if $n \ne p$. Thus e^0 and e are two symbols for the same member of $\mathfrak{R}$.

Since a function is a set, the meaning of equality in $\mathfrak{R}$ is clear from the discussion in Article 2 of Chapter 1. It is easy to see that f and g are *equal* if and only if $f(n) = g(n)$ for all $n \in I_\omega$. An obvious consequence is the following, which guarantees that $\mathfrak{R}$ consists of more than one member.

Theorem 1

$\theta \ne e$.

Order is defined in $\mathfrak{R}$ *lexicographically*, and we begin by defining the relation *less than*. For members f and g of $\mathfrak{R}$, $f < g$ if and only if there is some $m \in I_\omega$ such that $f(m) < g(m)$ and $f(n) = g(n)$ for $0 \le n < m$. Clearly, $\theta < e^p$ and $e^{p+1} < e^p$ for all p; also,

$f < g$ implies $f \neq g$. As usual, f is *positive* if $\theta < f$ and *negative* if $f < \theta$.

Example 2 $(-4,9,7,6, \ldots)$ is less than $(-3,0,0, \ldots)$; $(-3,1,0,7, \ldots)$ is less than $(-3,1,2,7, \ldots)$; and $(4,2,9,8, \ldots)$ is less than $(4,3,0,0, \ldots)$.

Theorem 2

The relation $<$ in $\mathfrak{R}$ is transitive.

Proof Suppose $f < g$ and $g < h$. Let m_1 be such that $f(m_1) < g(m_1)$ while $f(n) = g(n)$ for $0 \leq n < m_1$; and let m_2 satisfy $g(m_2) < h(m_2)$ and $g(n) = h(n)$ for $0 \leq n < m_2$. Taking $m = \min \{m_1, m_2\}$, we see that $f(m) < h(m)$ and $f(n) = h(n)$ for $0 \leq n < m$ ▲

We define the relation $\leq$ in $\mathfrak{R}$ by agreeing that, for $f,g \in \mathfrak{R}$, $f \leq g$ if and only if $f < g$ or $f = g$. From this definition follows immediately the usual fact that $f < g$ if and only if $f \leq g$ and $f \neq g$.

Theorem 3

The relation $\leq$ in $\mathfrak{R}$ is a linear order.

Proof Clearly $f \leq f$; that is, the relation is reflexive. From the definition of less than it follows that $f < g$ and $g < f$ is impossible. Hence $f \leq g$ and $g \leq f$ imply $f = g$; that is, it is an antisymmetric relation. Transitivity is an easy consequence of Theorem 2.
　　To see that the order is linear, suppose $f \neq g$ and consider $\{n : n \in I_\omega$ and $f(n) \neq g(n)\}$. This set is nonempty and bounded below; hence it has a minimum m. From $f(m) \neq g(m)$ and $f(n) = g(n)$ for $0 \leq n < m$ follows $f < g$ or $g < f$ ▲

It is easy to see that the least member law does not hold in the set $\mathfrak{R}$; for instance, the set $\{e^p : p \in I_\omega\}$ is nonempty and is bounded below by θ but does not have a minimum. However, the real numbers are *complete* in the sense that they possess the following property.

Theorem 4

A nonempty subset of $\mathfrak{R}$ that is bounded below has an infimum.

Proof Let S be a nonempty subset of $\mathfrak{R}$ that is bounded below by g. Then the set $A_0 = \{f(0): f \in S\}$ is nonempty and is bounded below by $g(0)$. It follows that A_0 has a minimum; call this a_0. Let $S_0 = \{f: f \in S$ and $f(0) = a_0\}$ so that S_0 is a nonempty subset of S.

Now proceed inductively. Assume that members $a_0 \in I$ and $a_1, \ldots, a_n \in I_9$ have been defined and that $S_n = \{f: f \in S$ and $f(m) = a_m$ for $0 \le m \le n\}$ is not empty. Then $A_{n+1} = \{f(n+1): f \in S_n\}$ is nonempty and is bounded below by 0 since $A_{n+1} \subset I_9$. Hence $a_{n+1} = \min A_{n+1}$ exists and is a member of I_9; also, $S_{n+1} = \{f: f \in S$ and $f(m) = a_m$ for $0 \le m \le n+1\}$ is not empty. It follows that a_n is defined for all n with $a_0 \in I$ and $a_n \in I_9$ for $n \ge 1$.

It is clear that the function h defined for $n \in I_\omega$ by $h(n) = a_n$ satisfies conditions (a) and (b) of (1). Suppose the third condition of the list to fail; that is, assume there is some $m \in I_\omega$ with $h(n) = 9$ for all $n > m$. Let f be a member of S_{m+1}; thus $f(m+1) = a_{m+1} = 9$. Since $f \in \mathfrak{R}$, there is some $p > m$ for which $f(p) \ne 9$; and, without loss of generality, we may assume p to be the least such integer. Then $f(p) < 9$ and $f(n) = 9$ for $m + 1 \le n < p$. From this and the fact that $f \in S_{m+1}$, it follows that $f \in S_{p-1}$; hence $a_p = \min A_p \le f(p) < 9$. This contradiction leads us to conclude that condition (c) of (1) holds; thus h is a real number.

From its definition it can be seen that h is a lower bound of S. This can be verified formally by observing that if $f \in S$ and $f(m) < h(m) = a_m$ while $f(n) = h(n) = a_n$ for $0 \le n < m$, then $f \in S_{m-1}$ and $f(m) < \min A_m$, a contradiction. Thus if $f \in S$, then $h \le f$.

Finally, we prove that h is the infimum of S. To this end, let $g \in \mathfrak{R}$ be such that $h < g$ so that, for some m, $h(m) < g(m)$ and $h(n) = g(n)$ for $0 \le n < m$. Then for any $f \in S_m$ it follows from

$f(n) = h(n)$ for $0 \leq n \leq m$ that $f < g$; hence g is not a lower bound of S ▲

Remark   For a more formal application of the recursion theorem, one might define the quantities V, c, and f of that theorem as follows.   Take V to be the collection of nonempty subsets of $\mathfrak{R}$, and let c be the set S of the preceding proof. Define a function π on V into $\mathfrak{R}$ by taking $\pi(T) = \min$ $\{h(0) : h \in T\}$ for each T in V.   Next, define φ and σ on V into V by $\varphi(T) = \{h : h \in T$ and $h(0) = \pi(T)\}$ and $\sigma(T) = \{k : k \in \mathfrak{R}$ and, for some $h \in T$, $k(n) = h(n + 1)$ for $n \in I_\omega\}$.   Finally, take $f(T) = \sigma(\varphi(T))$ for $T \in V$.   It follows that $g(n)$ exists for $n \in I_\omega$, and it can be verified that $\pi(g(n))$ is the quantity a_n in the above proof.

3   THE SET $\mathfrak{R}_\omega$

In this article we consider those real numbers that "terminate in zeros."   For each $k \in I_\omega$ let

$$\mathfrak{R}_k = \{f : f \in \mathfrak{R} \text{ and } f(n) = 0 \text{ for } n > k\}.$$

Obviously $\theta, e \in \mathfrak{R}_k$ and $\mathfrak{R}_k \subset \mathfrak{R}_{k+1}$ for all k.   Further, let

$$\mathfrak{R}_\omega = \cup_{k \in I_\omega} \mathfrak{R}_k.$$

Then $\mathfrak{R}_\omega$ is a subset of $\mathfrak{R}$; but there exist real numbers that are not in $\mathfrak{R}_\omega$, one such being the function f given by $f(n) = 1$ for all n.
For $f \in \mathfrak{R}_k$, define

$$F_k = \sum_{s=0}^{k} 10^{k-s} f(s)$$

and call F_k the *k-image* of f.   The function defined on $\mathfrak{R}_k$ into I by taking F_k as the image of f is called the *k-mapping* of $\mathfrak{R}_k$ into I.   It is easy to see that for all $k \in I_\omega$

θ has k-image 0,

e has k-image 10^k.

Example 3   For members $f = (-6,9,7,0,0, \ldots)$ and $g = (4,1,6,0,0, \ldots)$ of $\Re_2$, the 2-images are $F_2 = -503$ and $G_2 = 416$. Since f and g are members of $\Re_3$ also, we have $F_3 = -5030$ and $G_3 = 4160$.

The k-mapping is a natural one to consider for, as we prove next, it is *order-preserving;* that is, $f \le g$ if and only if $F_k \le G_k$, where F_k and G_k are the k-images of f and g, respectively.

Theorem 5

The k-mapping of $\Re_k$ into I is order-preserving and is a one-to-one mapping onto I.

Proof   First let us observe that the mapping is onto I. If $a \in I$, then, by Theorem 33 of Chapter 5, we may write $a = \displaystyle\sum_{s=0}^{k} 10^{k-s} a_s$ with $a_0 \in I$ and $a_n \in I_9$ for $1 \le n \le k$. Clearly the function h defined on I_ω by $h(n) = a_n$ for $0 \le n \le k$ and $h(n) = 0$ for $n > k$ is a member of $\Re_k$, and it has k-image a.

Next we establish that $f,g \in \Re_k$ with $f < g$ implies $F_k < G_k$, where F_k and G_k are the k-images of f and g, respectively. Not only will this imply that order is preserved, but it will also show that distinct members of $\Re_k$ have distinct images, thereby proving the mapping to be one-to-one. Since $f(n) = g(n) = 0$ for $n > k$, $f < g$ implies that there is some m less than or equal to k such that $f(m) < g(m)$ and $f(n) = g(n)$ for $0 \le n < m$. Hence

$$G_k - F_k = \sum_{s=m}^{k} 10^{k-s}[g(s) - f(s)]$$

and $g(m) - f(m) > 0$. From Theorem 32 of Chapter 5, it follows that $F_k < G_k$ ▲

Since the k-mapping is one-to-one, it will be convenient to indicate corresponding quantities by writing $f \underset{k}{\longleftrightarrow} F_k$. We observe next the relationship between images under different mappings.

Theorem 6

For $j,k \in I_\omega$ with $j < k$, let $f \in \mathcal{R}_j$ [so that $f \in \mathcal{R}_k$ as well]. If $f \underset{j}{\longleftrightarrow} F_j$ and $f \underset{k}{\longleftrightarrow} F_k$, then $F_k = 10^{k-j}F_j$.

Proof

$$F_k = \sum_{s=0}^{k} 10^{k-s}f(s) = \sum_{s=0}^{j} 10^{k-s}f(s)$$

$$= 10^{k-j} \sum_{s=0}^{j} 10^{j-s}f(s) = 10^{k-j}F_j \; \blacktriangle$$

By using the k-mappings, it is possible to define *addition* and *multiplication* on $\mathcal{R}_\omega$. If $f,g \in \mathcal{R}_\omega$, there is some k such that $f,g \in \mathcal{R}_k$. As usual, let F_k and G_k be the k-images of f and g, respectively. Define $f + g$ to be the unique member of $\mathcal{R}_k$ such that

$$f + g \underset{k}{\longleftrightarrow} F_k + G_k,$$

and fg to be the unique member of $\mathcal{R}_{2k}$ such that

$$fg \underset{2k}{\longleftrightarrow} F_k G_k.$$

It is necessary, first of all, to confirm that the *sum* and *product* so defined do not depend on the choice of k. To do this, suppose also that $f,g \in \mathcal{R}_j$, where, without loss of generality, $j < k$. Let $r \in \mathcal{R}_j$ and $s \in \mathcal{R}_{2j}$ be such that

$$r \underset{j}{\longleftrightarrow} F_j + G_j$$

and

$$s \underset{2j}{\longleftrightarrow} F_j G_j.$$

Then by Theorem 6,

$$f + g \underset{k}{\longleftrightarrow} F_k + G_k = 10^{k-j}(F_j + G_j) \underset{k}{\longleftrightarrow} r$$

and

$$fg \underset{2k}{\longleftrightarrow} F_k G_k = 10^{2k-2j}F_j G_j \underset{2k}{\longleftrightarrow} s$$

so that $r = f + g$ and $s = fg$.

Example 4   With f and g as in Example 3,

$$f + g \underset{2}{\longleftrightarrow} F_2 + G_2 = -87 = -100 + 13$$

from which $f + g = (-1,1,3,0,0, \ldots)$.   Also

$$fg \underset{4}{\longleftrightarrow} F_2G_2 = -209248 = -210000 + 752;$$

hence $fg = (-21,0,7,5,2,0,0, \ldots)$.

Addition and multiplication in $\mathfrak{R}_\omega$ satisfy many of the rules that apply to integers; specifically, the following statements are valid for members f, g, and h of $\mathfrak{R}_\omega$.

1. $f + g = g + f$.
2. $f + (g + h) = (f + g) + h$.
3. $f + \theta = f$.
4. For any $f \in \mathfrak{R}_\omega$ there is a *negative* $-f \in \mathfrak{R}_\omega$ such that $f + (-f) = \theta$.
5. $fg = gf$.
6. $f(gh) = (fg)h$.
7. $fe = f$.
8. $fh = gh$ and $h \neq \theta$ imply $f = g$.
9. $f(g + h) = fg + fh$.
10. $\leq$ is a linear order in $\mathfrak{R}_\omega$.
11. $f \leq g$ implies $f + h \leq g + h$.
12. $f \leq g$ and $\theta \leq h$ imply $fh \leq gh$.
13. $\theta \neq e$.

The first of these statements is verified by observing that if $f,g \in \mathfrak{R}_k$, then

$$f + g \underset{k}{\longleftrightarrow} F_k + G_k = G_k + F_k \underset{k}{\longleftrightarrow} g + f.$$

Proofs of *2, 5, 6*, and *9* are similar.   Statements *3* and *7* are consequences of the fact that θ and e have k-images 0 and 10^k, respectively.   If F_k is the k-image of $f \in \mathfrak{R}_k$, let $-f$ be that member of $\mathfrak{R}_k$ whose k-image is $-F_k$; then $f + (-f) = \theta$ is immediate, and *4* is verified.   To prove *8*, let f, g, and h be members of $\mathfrak{R}_k$ having k-images F_k, G_k, and H_k, respectively.   Then $h \neq \theta$ implies $H_k \neq 0$, and $fh = gh$ implies $F_kH_k = G_kH_k$.   Combining these facts shows that $F_k = G_k$, from which $f = g$.   Statements *11* and *12* follow at once from the order-preserving character of k-mappings, while *10* and *13* are merely restatements for the set $\mathfrak{R}_\omega$ of earlier theorems.

From the above list of properties, it can be seen that the system $\mathfrak{R}_\omega$ is an ordered integral domain; hence the theorems in Articles 1, 2, and 4 of Chapter 5 are valid in this system.

4   APPROXIMATING FUNCTIONS

Our goal in the remaining part of this chapter is to extend the definitions of addition and multiplication from $\mathfrak{R}_\omega$ to all of $\mathfrak{R}$. This will be accomplished through use of so-called *approximating functions*, which we explore next.

For $f \in \mathfrak{R}$ and $k \in I_\omega$, the function f_k defined on I_ω by

$$f_k(n) = \begin{cases} f(n) & \text{if } n \le k \\ 0 & \text{if } n > k \end{cases}$$

is called the kth *approximation* to f. It is immediate that $f_k \in \mathfrak{R}_k$ and that $\theta \le f$ implies $\theta \le f_k$. Also, if $j \le k$, then $f_j \le f_k \le f$.

Theorem 7

If $j,k \in I_\omega$ and $j \le k$, then $f_k < f_j + e^j$.

Proof   Let $f_k \xleftrightarrow{k} F_k$ and $f_j \xrightarrow{j} F_j$ so that $f_j + e^j \xleftrightarrow{k} 10^{k-j}(F_j + 1)$. By using Theorem 31 of Chapter 5 it is easy to verify that $F_k < 10^{k-j}(F_j + 1)$, and $f_k < f_j + e^j$ follows from the order-preserving character of k-mappings ▲

A special case of Theorem 7, which we shall use several times, is that $f_k \le f_0 + e$ for any k in I_ω.

Theorem 8

$f < g$ if and only if $f < g_k$ for some $k \in I_\omega$.

Proof   If $f < g_k$, then $f < g$ since $g_k \le g$. If $f < g$, then, for some m, $f(m) < g(m)$ and $f(n) = g(n)$ for $0 \le n < m$; hence $f < g_m$ ▲

From this result it follows that $\mathfrak{R}_\omega$ is *dense* in $\mathfrak{R}$; in other words, between any two distinct members of $\mathfrak{R}$ is a member of $\mathfrak{R}_\omega$. This property of real numbers is of considerable importance, for it is precisely this that makes possible the definition of addition and multiplication on $\mathfrak{R}$ in terms of those operations on $\mathfrak{R}_\omega$. In later developments, this density of $\mathfrak{R}_\omega$ will make its appearance through the result we establish next, namely, that every function is determined by its approximating functions.

Theorem 9

$$f = \sup\ \{f_k \colon\ \ k \in I_\omega\}.$$

Proof Clearly this supremum exists and does not exceed f. Also, if $h < f$, then $h < f_k$ for some k; hence h is not an upper bound of the set ▲

Corollary

$$f \le f_j + e^j \text{ for all } j.$$

Proof By Theorem 7, $f_j + e^j$ is an upper bound of the set $\{f_k \colon k \in I_\omega\}$; hence $f \le f_j + e^j$ from the theorem ▲

5 ADDITION

If f and g are both in $\mathfrak{R}_\omega$, then the sum $f + g$ is defined; and for some j, $f = f_j$ and $g = g_j$ so that $f + g = f_j + g_j$. It follows that $f + g = \sup\ \{f_k + g_k \colon\ \ k \in I_\omega\}$. This suggests a natural way in which to extend *addition* to the set of all real numbers.

For any f and g in $\mathfrak{R}$, the nonempty set $\{f_k + g_k \colon\ \ k \in I_\omega\}$ is bounded above since $f_k + g_k \le (f_0 + e) + (g_0 + e)$. Hence the set has a supremum which we denote by $f + g$ and call the *sum* of f and g; that is,

$$f + g = \sup\ \{f_k + g_k \colon\ \ k \in I_\omega\}.$$

The remarks in the paragraph above ensure that this definition of sum agrees with the one given earlier in the event f and g are in $\mathfrak{R}_\omega$.

Example 5   Let f and g be members of $\Re$ with $f(n) = 1$ and $g(2n) = 0$, $g(2n + 1) = 9$ for $n \in I_\omega$.   Then

$$f_0 + g_0 = (1,0, \ldots)$$
$$f_1 + g_1 = (2,0,0, \ldots)$$
$$f_2 + g_2 = (2,0,1,0, \ldots)$$
$$f_3 + g_3 = (2,0,2,0,0, \ldots)$$
$$f_4 + g_4 = (2,0,2,0,1,0, \ldots)$$
$$\cdots \cdots \cdots \cdots \cdots \cdots$$

and it follows that $f + g$ is the function $(2,0,2,0,2,0, \ldots)$ in which 0 and 2 alternate.

The following theorems apply to any members f, g, and h of $\Re$ and are immediate consequences of the above definition.

Theorem 10

$$f + g = g + f.$$

Proof   For each k, f_k and g_k are members of $\Re_k$ so that the rules of Article 3 may be applied.   Thus $f_k + g_k = g_k + f_k$, from which $\{f_k + g_k: \ k \in I_\omega\} = \{g_k + f_k: \ k \in I_\omega\}$ ▲

Theorem 11

$$f + \theta = f.$$

Proof   For each k, $f_k + \theta_k = f_k$ ▲

Theorem 12

$$f \le g \text{ implies } f + h \le g + h.$$

Proof   It follows from $f \le g$ that $f_k \le g_k$ for each k; as a result $f_k + h_k \le g_k + h_k$ ▲

Corollary

$$f \le g \text{ and } h \le i \text{ imply } f + h \le g + i.$$

Before turning to associativity, we establish some specialized results for use in the proofs to follow.

Theorem 13

Let $p \geq 1$ be such that $g(p) < 9$. Then $g + e^p = h$, where $h(n) = g(n)$ for $n \neq p$ and $h(p) = g(p) + 1$.

Proof Using the k-mappings, we see that $h_k = g_k + e^p{}_k$ for every k in I_ω. It follows that $h = \sup \{h_k: \ k \in I_\omega\} = \sup \{g_k + e^p{}_k: k \in I_\omega\} = g + e^p$ ▲

Theorem 14

If $f \leq g + e^p$ for all $p \in I_\omega$, then $f \leq g$.

Proof Suppose that $g < f$ so that, for some m, $g(m) < f(m)$ while $g(n) = f(n)$ for all $0 \leq n < m$. Let p be an integer exceeding m for which $g(p) < 9$. From Theorem 13 it follows that $g + e^p = h$ is such that $h(n) = g(n) = f(n)$ for $0 \leq n < m$ and $h(m) = g(m) < f(m)$; that is, $g + e^p < f$ ▲

Theorem 15

$$f + (g + h) = (f + g) + h.$$

Proof For each k we may write $f_k + g_k + h_k$ without ambiguity since the functions concerned are in $\Re_\omega$. From $f_k + g_k + h_k = f_k + (g_k + h_k) \leq f + (g + h)$, it follows that $s = \sup \{f_k + g_k + h_k: \ k \in I_\omega\}$ exists and that $s \leq f + (g + h)$. Next we establish the reverse inequality.

For any $n, p \in I_\omega$, both $(g + h)_n$ and e^p are in $\Re_\omega$, enabling us to state that

$$(2) \qquad (g + h)_n - e^p < (g + h)_n \leq g + h.$$

The definition of sum ensures the existence of some k for which

$$(3) \qquad (g + h)_n - e^p < g_k + h_k,$$

and from the increasing nature of approximating functions we may assume $k \geq n$. This, in turn, implies $f_n \leq f_k$ so that, by using (3), we have

(4) $\qquad f_n + (g + h)_n \leq f_k + g_k + h_k + e^p \leq s + e^p.$

Since (4) holds for all n, it follows from the definition of sum that $f + (g + h) \leq s + e^p$ for all $p \in I_\omega$; hence $f + (g + h) \leq s$ by Theorem 14.

Combining the above results we have $f + (g + h) = \sup \{f_k + g_k + h_k \colon \; k \in I_\omega\}$. In the same manner, $(f + g) + h = \sup \{f_k + g_k + h_k \colon \; k \in I_\omega\}$, and associativity follows ▲

For any real number f, consider the set

$$A = \{h \colon \; h \in \mathfrak{R} \text{ and } f + h \leq \theta\}.$$

To see that this set is not empty, recall that $f \leq f_0 + e$; the latter function, being in $\mathfrak{R}_\omega$, has a negative, and that negative is a member of A. If $h \in A$, then $f_0 + h_0 \leq f + h \leq \theta$ so that $h \leq h_0 + e \leq -f_0 + e$, from which we conclude that A is bounded above. The supremum of A is the *negative* of f; that is,

$$-f = \sup \{h \colon \; h \in \mathfrak{R} \text{ and } f + h \leq \theta\}.$$

The suitability of this definition is shown next.

Theorem 16

$$f + (-f) = \theta.$$

Proof For $n, p \in I_\omega$, $(-f)_n - e^p < (-f)_n \leq -f$. From the definition of $-f$ it follows that there is some h with $(-f)_n - e^p < h$ and $f + h \leq \theta$. Thus $f_n + (-f)_n \leq f + h + e^p \leq e^p$ for all n and, by the definition of sum, $f + (-f) \leq e^p$. This holds for all p, from which we conclude $f + (-f) \leq \theta$.

The corollary of Theorem 9 ensures that $f \leq f_n + e^n$ for all n; thus $-f_n - e^n + f \leq \theta$. From the definition of negative we conclude that $-f_n - e^n \leq -f$; hence $\theta \leq f_n + (-f) + e^n \leq f + (-f) + e^n$ for all n. Therefore $\theta \leq f + (-f)$ ▲

The properties established so far show that $(\Re, +, \leq)$ is a linearly ordered group; thus the theorems and comments in Article 1 of Chapter 5 are applicable. In particular, it follows that the negative of f is unique, and consequently the definition of negative given here agrees with the earlier one in case f is a member of $\Re_\omega$.

6 MULTIPLICATION OF NONNEGATIVE NUMBERS

Let $\Re'$ be the set of nonnegative real numbers. Multiplication can be extended to this set in much the same way that addition was extended to $\Re$. This stems from the fact that if $f, g \in \Re' \cap \Re_\omega$, then $fg = \sup \{f_k g_k : k \in I_\omega\}$ since $f = f_k$ and $g = g_k$ for sufficiently large values of k. Using this as a guide, for $f, g \in \Re'$ consider the nonempty set $\{f_k g_k : k \in I_\omega\}$. This is bounded above since $f_k g_k \leq (f_0 + e)(g_0 + e)$. The *product* of f and g is

$$fg = \sup \{f_k g_k : k \in I_\omega\}.$$

Clearly this operation of *multiplication* is in agreement with that defined on $\Re_\omega$ earlier.

Example 6 With f and g as in Example 5,

$$f_0 g_0 = (0,0, \ . \ . \ .)$$
$$f_1 g_1 = (0,9,9,0, \ . \ . \ .)$$
$$f_2 g_2 = (0,9,9,9,0,0, \ . \ . \ .)$$
$$f_3 g_3 = (1,0,0,9,8,9,9,0, \ . \ . \ .)$$
$$f_4 g_4 = (1,0,0,9,9,8,9,9,0,0, \ . \ . \ .)$$
$$f_5 g_5 = (1,0,1,0,0,9,8,9,8,9,9,0, \ . \ . \ .)$$
$$. \ . \ . \ . \ . \ . \ . \ . \ . \ . \ . \ . \ . \ . \ . \ . \ . \ . \ . \ .$$

and $fg = (1,0,1,0,1,0, \ . \ . \ .)$ in which 0 and 1 alternate.

It can be seen that if $f, g \in \Re'$, then fg is in $\Re'$ as well. Also, $f\theta = \theta$ for any $f \in \Re'$. Proofs of the next three theorems are immediate.

Theorem 17

$fg = gf$ for $f, g \in \Re'$.

Theorem 18

$fe = f$ for $f \in \Re'$.

Theorem 19

$f \le g$ implies $fh \le gh$ for $f,g,h \in \Re'$.

Next, some preliminary results are given; the associative and distributive laws follow.

Theorem 20

If $h \in \Re_\omega$ and $m \in I_\omega$, then there is some $p \in I_\omega$ such that $he^p \le e^m$.

Proof   We shall consider only $h > \theta$, for otherwise we may take $p = 0$. Let k be such that $h \in \Re_k$, and let $h \overset{\longleftrightarrow}{\scriptstyle k} H_k$. Select p so that $p > m$, $p > k$, and $H_k 10^m \le 10^p$, as can be done by employing the corollary to Theorem 30 of Chapter 5. Then $he^p \overset{\longleftrightarrow}{\scriptstyle 2p} (10^{p-k}H_k)(1)$ and $e^m \overset{\longleftrightarrow}{\scriptstyle 2p} 10^{2p-m}$, so that $he^p \le e^m$ since $10^{p-k}H_k \le 10^p H_k \le 10^{2p-m}$ ▲

Theorem 21

If $f \in \Re$, $h \in \Re'$, and $f \le he^p$ for all $p \in I_\omega$, then $f \le \theta$.

Proof   Since $h_0 + e \in \Re_\omega$, for any $m \in I_\omega$ there is, by Theorem 20, some p such that $(h_0 + e)e^p \le e^m$. Thus $f \le he^p \le (h_0 + e)e^p \le e^m$. It follows from Theorem 14 that $f \le \theta$ ▲

Theorem 22

$f(gh) = (fg)h$ for $f,g,h \in \Re'$.

Proof   Since $f_k g_k h_k = f_k(g_k h_k) \le f(gh)$, it follows that $t = \sup \{f_k g_k h_k : k \in I_\omega\}$ exists and $t \le f(gh)$.

For $n,p \in I_\omega$, $(gh)_n - e^p < gh$; hence there is some k with $k \ge n$ and $(gh)_n - e^p < g_k h_k$. Since $f_n \le f_k$,

$$f_n(gh)_n \le f_k g_k h_k + f_k e^p \le t + fe^p$$

for all n. From this, $f(gh) \le t + fe^p$ for all p, which implies $f(gh) \le t$ by Theorem 21. It follows that $f(gh) = \sup \{f_k g_k h_k : k \in I_\omega\}$. In the same manner, $(fg)h = \sup \{f_k g_k h_k : k \in I_\omega\}$ ▲

Theorem 23

$f(g + h) = fg + fh$ for $f,g,h \in \Re'$.

Proof It is clear that $u = \sup \{f_k g_k + f_k h_k : k \in I_\omega\}$ exists and that $u \le f(g + h)$ and $u \le fg + fh$.

For $n,p \in I_\omega$ there is some $k \ge n$ such that $(g + h)_n - e^p \le g_k + h_k$. Hence

$$f_n(g + h)_n \le f_k g_k + f_k h_k + f_k e^p \le u + fe^p$$

for all n and p, so that $f(g + h) \le u$.

Similarly, for $n,p,s \in I_\omega$ there exist $i,j \in I_\omega$ such that $(fg)_n - e^p < f_i g_i$ and $(fh)_n - e^s < f_j h_j$. Letting $k = \max \{i,j\}$, we obtain

$$(fg)_n + (fh)_n < f_k g_k + f_k h_k + e^p + e^s < u + e^p + e^s,$$

from which $fg + fh \le u$. Combining results, we have $f(g + h) = u = fg + fh$ ▲

7 INVERSE OF POSITIVE NUMBERS

For a positive real number f, let $B = \{h : h \in \Re' \text{ and } fh \le e\}$. The set B cannot be empty, for then $e < fe^p$ for all $p \in I_\omega$, from which we obtain the contradiction $e \le \theta$ by applying Theorem 21.

To show that B is bounded above, let k be the least integer such that $\theta < f_k$ and define the real number c^k by $c^k(0) = 10^k$ and $c^k(n) = 0$ for $n \ge 1$. Then $c^k \in \Re_\omega$, and by examining k-images it readily follows that $c^k e^k = e$. Since $e^k \le f_k \le f$, $e = c^k e^k \le c^k f$. Thus if h is such that $c^k + e \le h$, then $c^k f + ef \le hf$ so that $e \le c^k f < hf$, and it follows that h is not a member of B. In other words, B is bounded above by $c^k + e$.

Since $\sup \{h : h \in \Re' \text{ and } fh \le e\}$ exists, we denote it by f^{-1} and call it the *inverse* of f. It is clear that f^{-1} is a member of

$\mathcal{R}'$ so that the product ff^{-1} has meaning from Article 6; we next show that this product has the value we expect.

Theorem 24

$$ff^{-1} = e.$$

Proof For $n \in I_\omega$, $f^{-1} < f^{-1} + e^n$ and, since the latter number is positive, we conclude from the definition of f^{-1} that $e < f(f^{-1} + e^n) = ff^{-1} + fe^n$; thus $e \leq ff^{-1}$ by Theorem 21. On the other hand, for $n \in I_\omega$, $f^{-1} - e^n < f^{-1}$ so that there is some h with $f^{-1} - e^n < h$ and $fh \leq e$. From this, $ff^{-1} - fe^n \leq fh \leq e$ so that $ff^{-1} \leq e$ by the same theorem ▲

8 MULTIPLICATION

The *absolute value* $|f|$ of a real number f is defined to be

$$|f| = \begin{cases} f & \text{if } f \geq \theta \\ -f & \text{if } f < \theta. \end{cases}$$

Since $-f$ is positive if f is negative, the absolute value of a number is always nonnegative. It can be seen that $|f| = |-f|$ and, by considering cases, that $|f| = |g|$ implies $f = g$ or $f = -g$.

Using the notion of absolute value, we define *multiplication* on $\mathcal{R}$ by stating that the *product* fg of real numbers f and g is

$$fg = \begin{cases} |f|\,|g| & \text{if } f,g \in \mathcal{R}' \text{ or if } -f,-g \in \mathcal{R}', \\ -|f|\,|g| & \text{otherwise.} \end{cases}$$

[Here and throughout this article $-hk$ means $-(hk)$.] Obviously this agrees with the definition of multiplication on $\mathcal{R}'$ given previously. Also it is clear that $f\theta = \theta$ for any $f \in \mathcal{R}$.

Theorem 25

$$|fg| = |f|\,|g|.$$

Proof If $fg = |f|\,|g|$, then $|fg| = |\,|f|\,|g|\,| = |f|\,|g|$. Otherwise $|fg| = |-|f|\,|g|\,| = |f|\,|g|$ ▲

Theorem 26

$$(-f)g = f(-g) = -(fg).$$

Proof From Theorem 25, $(-f)g$, $f(-g)$, and $-(fg)$ all have the same absolute value. It is easy to verify that all three expressions equal $-|f|\,|g|$ if $f,g \in \mathfrak{R}'$ or if $-f,-g \in \mathfrak{R}'$. Otherwise all three are equal to $|f|\,|g|$, as can be seen by considering the various possibilities ▲

Theorem 27

$$(-f)(-g) = fg.$$

Proof The proof is immediate from the definition of product ▲

Next we establish three basic properties of multiplication.

Theorem 28

$$fg = gf.$$

Proof Using the commutative law in $\mathfrak{R}'$, we see that if $f,g \in \mathfrak{R}'$ or if $-f,-g \in \mathfrak{R}'$, then $fg = |f|\,|g| = |g|\,|f| = gf$. Otherwise, $fg = -|f|\,|g| = -|g|\,|f| = gf$ ▲

Theorem 29

$$f(gh) = (fg)h.$$

Proof By Theorem 25 both $f(gh)$ and $(fg)h$ have absolute value $|f|\,|g|\,|h|$. If all or exactly one of f, g, and h is in $\mathfrak{R}'$, then

$$f(gh) = |f|\,|g|\,|h| = (fg)h.$$

Otherwise,

$$f(gh) = -|f|\,|g|\,|h| = (fg)h \ ▲$$

Theorem 30

$$fe = f.$$

Proof This is clear if $f \in \mathfrak{R}'$. Otherwise $fe = -(-f)e = -(-f)$ $= f$ ▲

The distributive law is established by considering first a special case.

Theorem 31

If $p,q \in \mathfrak{R}'$, then $f(p - q) = fp - fq$ for any $f \in \mathfrak{R}$.

Proof First, suppose that $f \in \mathfrak{R}'$. If $p \geq q$, then $p = (p - q) + q$ with both $p - q$ and q members of $\mathfrak{R}'$. Hence we may apply the distributive law in $\mathfrak{R}'$ to obtain

$$fp = f[(p - q) + q] = f(p - q) + fq$$

from which $f(p - q) = fp - fq$ follows. If $q > p$, then $q = (q - p) + p$ with $(q - p), p \in \mathfrak{R}'$ so that

$$fq = f[(q - p) + p] = f(q - p) + fp.$$

From this, $-fq = -f(q - p) - fp$ so that $fp - fq = -f(q - p) = f(p - q)$ by virtue of Theorem 26 and Theorem 2 of Chapter 5.

Next, suppose that $f \notin \mathfrak{R}'$. Then $-f \in \mathfrak{R}'$ and, using the previous paragraph,

$$(-f)(p - q) = (-f)p - (-f)q = (-f)p + fq.$$

But then $-(-f)(p - q) = -(-f)p - fq$, from which $f(p - q) = fp - fq$ ▲

Theorem 32

$$f(g + h) = fg + fh.$$

Proof Define g_1 and h_1 by

$$g_1 = \begin{cases} g & \text{if } g \geq \theta \\ \theta & \text{if } g < \theta \end{cases}, \qquad h_1 = \begin{cases} h & \text{if } h \geq \theta \\ \theta & \text{if } h < \theta \end{cases};$$

and define g_2 and h_2 by $g_2 = g_1 - g$ and $h_2 = h_1 - h$. Then it is easy to see that g_1, g_2, h_1, and h_2 are all in $\mathfrak{R}'$; also that $g = g_1 - g_2$ and $h = h_1 - h_2$. From this, $g + h = (g_1 + h_1) - (g_2 + h_2)$ with both $g_1 + h_1$ and $g_2 + h_2$ members of $\mathcal{R}'$. From Theorem 31 and the distributive law in $\mathcal{R}'$, it follows that

$$
\begin{aligned}
f(g + h) &= f[(g_1 + h_1) - (g_2 + h_2)] \\
&= f(g_1 + h_1) - f(g_2 + h_2) \\
&= (fg_1 + fh_1) - (fg_2 + fh_2) \\
&= (fg_1 - fg_2) + (fh_1 - fh_2) \\
&= f(g_1 - g_2) + f(h_1 - h_2) \\
&= fg + fh \ \blacktriangle
\end{aligned}
$$

It is now a simple matter to show that multiplication interacts with order properly.

Theorem 33

$f \leq g$ and $\theta \leq h$ imply $fh \leq gh$.

Proof From $f \leq g$ follows $\theta \leq g - f$. Since $g - f$ and h are both in $\mathcal{R}'$, so is $(g - f)h = [g + (-f)]h = gh + (-f)h = gh - fh$. But then $\theta \leq gh - fh$ implies $fh \leq gh$ $\blacktriangle$

Lastly, the *inverse* of a negative real number f is defined to be $f^{-1} = -(-f)^{-1}$.

Theorem 34

If $f \neq \theta$, then $ff^{-1} = e$.

Proof This has already been shown for positive f. If f is negative, then so is f^{-1} from the definition above. Hence $ff^{-1} = |f| \, |f^{-1}| = (-f)(-f)^{-1} = e$ $\blacktriangle$

Corollary

If $fh = gh$ and $h \neq \theta$, then $f = g$.

This completes the definition of the real number system. It is not our intention to go beyond this definition except in one respect: to prove that the real number system is unique.

EXERCISES AND EXTENSIONS

1. Show that $f \in \mathcal{R}$ is negative if and only if $f(0) < 0$.   Is it true that f is positive if and only if $f(0) > 0$?

2. Use the definition of addition and multiplication to verify the following:

   (*a*) $(2,1,3,0,0, \ldots) + (-4,0,1,0,0, \ldots)$
   $$= (-2,1,4,0,0, \ldots).$$
   (*b*) $(3,1,4,0,0, \ldots) + (-2,9,9,0,0, \ldots)$
   $$= (2,1,3,0,0, \ldots).$$
   (*c*) $(1,2,3,0,0, \ldots)(4,5,0,0, \ldots) = (5,5,3,5,0,0, \ldots)$.
   (*d*) $(-2,1,0,0, \ldots)(-1,5,0,0, \ldots) = (0,9,5,0,0, \ldots)$.

3. Use the definition of addition and multiplication to verify the following:

   (*a*) $(0,1,1,1,1, \ldots) + (0,2,2,2,2, \ldots) = (0,3,3,3,3, \ldots)$.
   (*b*) $(0,1,1,1,1, \ldots)(0,6,0,0,0, \ldots) = (0,0,6,6,6,6, \ldots)$.

4. Find the negative of $(0,2,2,2,2, \ldots)$.

5. For $f \notin \mathcal{R}_\omega$, let g be defined on I_ω by $g(0) = -f(0) - 1$, and $g(n) = 9 - f(n)$ for $n > 0$.   Prove that $g \in \mathcal{R}$ and that $g = -f$.

6. Find the inverse of $(0,1,1,1,1, \ldots)$.

7. Prove that a nonempty subset of $\mathcal{R}$ which is bounded above has a supremum.

8. Prove that the set $\mathcal{R}$ is noncountable. [SUGGESTION: See Exercise 21 of Chapter 5.]

9. Prove that the subset $\mathcal{R}_0$ of the system of real numbers is isomorphic with the system I of integers.   Because of this we shall refer to the real numbers of $\mathcal{R}_0$ as *integers*.

10. [*Principle of Archimedes*] For $f,g \in \mathcal{R}$ with $g > \theta$ there is an integer $h \in \mathcal{R}_0$ such that $f < gh$.

11. Let f be a nonnegative real number and assume that $f \leq g$ whenever $g > \theta$.   Prove that $f = \theta$.

A number f of $\mathfrak{R}$ is *repeating* if there are integers t and s, t positive and s nonnegative, such that $f(n) = f(n + t)$ for $n \geq s$.

12. Prove that f is repeating if and only if $-f$ is.

13. Prove that if f is repeating, then there are integers $g,h \in \mathfrak{R}_0$ such that $f = g^{-1}h$. [SUGGESTION: Let $g^*(0) = 10^t$, $g^*(n) = 0$ for $n > 0$, and show that $fg^* - f \in \mathfrak{R}_{s-1}$. Use this to obtain an appropriate g and h.]

14. Prove that if $f = g^{-1}h$ with $g,h \in \mathfrak{R}_0$, $g \neq \theta$, then f is repeating. [SUGGESTION: Let $a = h(0)$ and $b = g(0)$; without loss of generality assume $b > 0$. From the division algorithm $a = bq_1 + r_1$, $10\, r_1 = bq_2 + r_2$, . . . , $10\, r_n = bq_{n+1} + r_{n+1}$, . . . with $0 \leq r_n < b$. This last condition ensures that the remainders ultimately repeat. Use this and the fact that $f(n) = q_n$ to show that f is repeating.]

A function from I_ω into $\mathfrak{R}$ is called a *sequence* and is denoted by $\{f_n\}$, where f_n is the image of the function at n. A sequence $\{f_n\}$ *converges* to a *limit* f if, for each positive g, there is an integer N such that $|f_n - f| < g$ for $n \geq N$. If $f_n = \sum_{s=0}^{n} h_s$ for all n, the limit of the sequence $\{f_n\}$ is usually denoted by $\sum_{s=0}^{\infty} h_s$ and is referred to as the *sum* of an *infinite series*.

15. Prove that the limit of a sequence, if it exists, is unique.

16. The sequence $\{f_n\}$ is *increasing* if $f_n \leq f_{n+1}$ for all n and is *bounded* if $\{f_n : n \in I_\omega\}$ is a bounded set. Prove that an increasing sequence is convergent if and only if it is bounded.

In part the following exercises use *standard notation* for the real numbers. Thus the quantity fg^{-1} is written $\dfrac{f}{g}$; the real number e^p for

$p \in I_\omega$ is written 10^{-p} or $\dfrac{1}{10^p}$; and θ is denoted
by 0.

17. Let f be a positive real number.   (*a*) By induction of k, prove
that $\displaystyle\sum_{s=0}^{k} \frac{f(s)}{10^s} = f_k$.   (*b*) Conclude from (*a*) that $f = \displaystyle\sum_{s=0}^{\infty} \frac{f(s)}{10^s}$.
[This infinite series is referred to as the *decimal representation*
of the real number f; in the usual notation it is written simply
$f(0) . f(1)f(2) \cdot \cdot \cdot f(n) \cdot \cdot \cdot \cdot$.   For example, the real number
$(3,1,4,1,5,9, \ldots)$ has the decimal representation 3.14159
$\cdot \cdot \cdot$.]

18. Discuss the modification that must be made in Exercise 17 if f
is negative.   Also, discuss the decimal representation of a
negative real number.

19. Prove that the equation $x^2 = a$ has at most two solutions in $\Re$.

20. Prove that the equation $x^2 = a$ has a nonnegative solution in
$\Re$ for any nonnegative real number a.   [SUGGESTION: Show
that it is sufficient to consider $a > 1$.   Let $A = \{x:\ x \in \Re,$
$x \geq 0,\ x^2 \leq a\}$.   Show that A is not empty and is bounded
above; hence it has a supremum s.   Let $t = \dfrac{as + a}{a + s}$.   Show
that if one assumes $s^2 < a$, then $s < t$ and $t^2 < a$, contrary to
the definition of s.   Similarly, show that the assumption $a < s^2$
leads to a contradiction.]

21. Show that $ax^2 + bx + c = 0$ $(a \neq 0)$ has a solution in $\Re$ if
and only if $b^2 - 4ac \geq 0$.

Uniqueness of the Real Number System

Chapter Seven
Uniqueness of the Real Number System

1 ORDERED FIELDS

An *ordered field* is an ordered quadruple $(F, +, \cdot, \leq)$ consisting of a set F, operations $+$ and $\cdot$ on F, and an order relation $\leq$ in F such that the following are satisfied.

F1. The ordered quadruple $(F, +, \cdot, \leq)$ is an ordered integral domain.

F2. To each nonzero member f of F there corresponds a member f^{-1} of F, called the *inverse* of f, such that $ff^{-1} = e$.

An ordered field is a *complete ordered field* if it has the following additional property.

F3. Any nonempty subset of F that is bounded below has an infimum.

It will be convenient to denote the ordered field $(F, +, \cdot, \leq)$, whether complete or not, simply by F; that is, the symbol for the set will be used for the system also.

In the preceding chapter we defined the real numbers, and the various properties proved there establish that system to be a complete ordered field. That is, we have demonstrated the existence of a complete ordered field by actually constructing such a system. It is our aim in this chapter to show that all complete ordered fields are intrinsically the same, in other words, that the real numbers are unique.

From *F1* it follows that in an ordered field we may invoke various theorems that were established in Chapter 5, and we shall do so without always making specific references. Also, the inverse of a nonzero member f is unique; for if $fg = e$ and $fh = e = hf$, then $g = eg = hfg = he = h$. Other familiar rules for the inverse are listed next.

Theorem 1

(a) $f \neq \theta$ implies $(-f)^{-1} = -f^{-1}$.

(b) $\theta < f$ implies $\theta < f^{-1}$, and $f < \theta$ implies $f^{-1} < \theta$.

(c) $f \neq \theta$ implies $(f^{-1})^{-1} = f$.

(d) $f \neq \theta$ and $g \neq \theta$ imply $(fg)^{-1} = f^{-1}g^{-1}$.

(e) $\theta < f < g$ implies $g^{-1} < f^{-1}$.

Proof   (a) $f \neq \theta$ implies $-f \neq \theta$ so that $(-f)^{-1}$ exists. Since $(-f)(-f^{-1}) = ff^{-1} = e$, $-f^{-1} = (-f)^{-1}$ from the uniqueness of the inverse.   (b) $\theta < f$ and $f^{-1} \leq \theta$ imply $ff^{-1} \leq f\theta$ or $e \leq \theta$, a contradiction. $f < \theta$ implies $\theta < -f$ and so $\theta < (-f)^{-1} = -f^{-1}$ and $f^{-1} < \theta$.   (c) $f \neq \theta$ implies $f^{-1} \neq \theta$ by (b); hence $(f^{-1})^{-1}$ exists. Then $(f^{-1})^{-1} = f$ follows from $ff^{-1} = f^{-1}f = e$ and the uniqueness of the inverse.   (d) $f \neq \theta$ and $g \neq \theta$ imply $fg \neq \theta$, so that $(fg)^{-1}$ exists. Then $(fg)^{-1} = f^{-1}g^{-1}$ follows from the fact that $fgf^{-1}g^{-1} = e$. (e) $\theta < f < g$ implies $\theta < f^{-1}$ and $\theta < g^{-1}$ so that $e = ff^{-1} < gf^{-1}$; hence $g^{-1} = g^{-1}e < g^{-1}gf^{-1} = f^{-1}$ ▲

If the ordered field is complete so that $F3$ is valid, the dual to that statement holds as well.

Theorem 2

In a complete ordered field any nonempty subset that is bounded above has a supremum.

Proof   Let A be a nonempty subset of a complete ordered field and assume A to be bounded above. Then $B = \{x: \ -x \in A\}$ is nonempty and is bounded below; hence it has an infimum by $F3$. By Theorem 8 of Chapter 5, A has a supremum, and it is equal to $-\inf B$ ▲

2 THE RATIONAL SUBFIELD

For any member f of an ordered field F and for any positive integer n, we write $n \circ f$ for the sum of n terms each equal to f. Then for any positive integers n, n_1, and n_2 we have the following:

(1)
    (a) $n \circ f > \theta$ if $f > \theta$.
    (b) $n_1 \circ f + n_2 \circ f = (n_1 + n_2) \circ f$.
    (c) $n \circ (fg) = (n \circ f)g$.
    (d) $n_1 \circ (n_2 \circ f) = (n_1 n_2) \circ f$.
    (e) $n_1 \circ e = n_2 \circ e$ if and only if $n_1 = n_2$.

[Here we have written $n_1 \circ f + n_2 \circ f$ for $(n_1 \circ f) + (n_2 \circ f)$.] The first four of these statements follow readily by induction on n or n_1. In one direction, (e) is obvious; for the other, suppose that $n_2 > n_1$. Then $n_1 \circ e + (n_2 - n_1) \circ e > n_1 \circ e$ by using (a); hence by (b) we have $n_2 \circ e > n_1 \circ e$, and (e) follows.

Because of (c) the symbol $n \circ fg$ is not ambiguous. Since there can be only one interpretation, we shall frequently write $n_1 n_2 \circ f$ for $(n_1 n_2) \circ f$.

The above definitions can be extended by letting $0 \circ f = \theta$ and by letting $m \circ f$ be $-((-m) \circ f)$ if m is a negative integer; thus the symbol $m \circ f$ has meaning for any integer m. By considering various cases it is easy to see that (b) through (e) of (1) remain valid when n, n_1, and n_2 are arbitrary integers. A similar result is the following.

Theorem 3

$(m_1 \circ e)(m_2 \circ e) = m_1 m_2 \circ e$ for any integers m_1 and m_2.

Proof By using (c) and (d),

$$(m_1 \circ e)(m_2 \circ e) = m_1 \circ [e(m_2 \circ e)] = m_1 \circ (m_2 \circ e) = m_1 m_2 \circ e \;\blacktriangle$$

If m and n are integers with n positive, then $(n \circ e)^{-1}$ exists, and we write $\dfrac{m \circ e}{n \circ e}$ for $(m \circ e)(n \circ e)^{-1}$. It is immediate that

$\dfrac{n \circ e}{n \circ e} = e$ for any positive integer n. Also, $\dfrac{m \circ e}{n \circ e} = \theta$ if and only if $m \circ e = \theta$, and this holds if and only if $m = 0$. The following is of the same nature.

Theorem 4

Let n and q be positive integers. Then $\dfrac{m \circ e}{n \circ e} < \dfrac{p \circ e}{q \circ e}$ if and only if $mq < np$.

Proof Since $n \circ e > \theta$ and $q \circ e > \theta$, $\dfrac{m \circ e}{n \circ e} < \dfrac{p \circ e}{q \circ e}$ if and only if $(m \circ e)(q \circ e) < (n \circ e)(p \circ e)$ or $mq \circ e < np \circ e$. In turn, this is true if and only if $\theta < (np \circ e) - (mq \circ e) = (np - mq) \circ e$, which holds if and only if $0 < np - mq$ ▲

Corollary

Let n and q be positive integers. Then $\dfrac{m \circ e}{n \circ e} = \dfrac{p \circ e}{q \circ e}$ if and only if $mq = np$.

The reader may have observed already that the elements we are considering behave much like "ordinary fractions." Further evidence to this effect is supplied through the investigation of sums and products.

Theorem 5

$$\frac{m \circ e}{n \circ e} + \frac{p \circ e}{q \circ e} = \frac{(mq + np) \circ e}{nq \circ e}.$$

Proof

$$
\begin{aligned}
\frac{m \circ e}{n \circ e} + \frac{p \circ e}{q \circ e} &= [(m \circ e)(q \circ e)][(n \circ e)(q \circ e)]^{-1} \\
&\quad + [(n \circ e)(p \circ e)][(n \circ e)(q \circ e)]^{-1} \\
&= (mq \circ e)(nq \circ e)^{-1} + (np \circ e)(nq \circ e)^{-1} \\
&= [(mq \circ e) + (np \circ e)](nq \circ e)^{-1} \\
&= [(mq + np) \circ e](nq \circ e)^{-1} \\
&= \frac{(mq + np) \circ e}{nq \circ e} \quad ▲
\end{aligned}
$$

Theorem 6

$$\left(\frac{m \circ e}{n \circ e}\right)\left(\frac{p \circ e}{q \circ e}\right) = \frac{mp \circ e}{nq \circ e}.$$

Proof

$$\left(\frac{m \circ e}{n \circ e}\right)\left(\frac{p \circ e}{q \circ e}\right) = [(m \circ e)(p \circ e)][(n \circ e)(q \circ e)]^{-1}$$
$$= (mp \circ e)(nq \circ e)^{-1}$$
$$= \frac{mp \circ e}{nq \circ e} \; \blacktriangle$$

The set R of all members of F of the form $\dfrac{m \circ e}{n \circ e}$ with m and n integers, n positive, is called the *rational subfield* of F; members of R are termed *rational numbers*. Use of the word "rational" in describing R is motivated by the fact that the members are ratios and the next theorem supplies justification for use of the term "subfield."

Theorem 7

R is an ordered field.

Proof   Theorems 5 and 6 show that the sum and product of members of R are themselves members of R; that is, R is *closed* under addition and multiplication. Since $\theta = \dfrac{0 \circ e}{1 \circ e}$ and $e = \dfrac{1 \circ e}{1 \circ e}$, both θ and e are in R. If $\dfrac{m \circ e}{n \circ e}$ is in R, then so is $\dfrac{(-m) \circ e}{n \circ e}$, and the latter is the negative of the former. If $m > 0$, the inverse of $\dfrac{m \circ e}{n \circ e}$ is $\dfrac{n \circ e}{m \circ e}$; if $m < 0$, it is $\dfrac{(-n) \circ e}{(-m) \circ e}$. In either event the inverse of a nonzero member of R is also a member of R. The remaining requirements for an ordered field are automatically satisfied by members of R because they are valid for all members of F $\blacktriangle$

3 DENSITY OF THE RATIONAL SUBFIELD

Hereafter we shall reserve symbols such as K and K^* for an ordered field that is known to be complete. It will evolve in the next article that the structure of a complete ordered field K is uniquely determined by its rational subfield R. This stems from the fact that the rational subfield is dense in K. Before establishing this property, we shall show that the principle of Archimedes, which was seen to apply to integers, is also valid in any complete ordered field.

Theorem 8

If $f,g \in K$ and $f > \theta$, then there is some positive integer m such that $g < m \circ f$.

Proof Suppose that this is not true. Then the nonempty set $A = \{n \circ f: \ n \in I \text{ and } n > 0\}$ is bounded above by g; consequently it has a supremum h and $h \leq g$. For any positive integer n, $(n + 1) \circ f \in A$ so that $(n + 1) \circ f \leq h$ or $n \circ f \leq h - f$. This implies that $h - f$ is an upper bound of A, contrary to the fact that $h - f < h$ ▲

Corollary

If $g \in K$ and if n is a positive integer, then there is an integer m such that $g < \dfrac{m \circ e}{n \circ e}$.

Proof Let $f = \dfrac{1 \circ e}{n \circ e}$. Since $f > \theta$, there is an integer m such that $g < m \circ f$. But $m \circ f = m \circ [(1 \circ e)(n \circ e)^{-1}] = [m \circ (1 \circ e)](n \circ e)^{-1}$ $= (m \circ e)(n \circ e)^{-1} = \dfrac{m \circ e}{n \circ e}$ ▲

Now we can establish that the rational subfield is a dense subset of the complete ordered field.

Theorem 9

Let R be the rational subfield of a complete ordered field K. If $f,g \in K$ with $f < g$, then there exists a member r of R such that $f < r < g$.

Proof Since $\theta < g - f$, there is some positive integer n such that $e < n \circ (g - f)$, from which

$$(2) \qquad\qquad \frac{1 \circ e}{n \circ e} < g - f.$$

Let A be the set of all integers m such that $g \leq \dfrac{m \circ e}{n \circ e}$. By the corollary to Theorem 8, A is not empty. Also, for some integer p, $-g < \dfrac{p \circ e}{n \circ e}$, so that $\dfrac{(-p) \circ e}{n \circ e} < \dfrac{m \circ e}{n \circ e}$ for all $m \in A$; and, as a consequence of Theorem 4, $-p < m$ for $m \in A$. We conclude that A is bounded below; hence it has a minimum $m' + 1$. But then $\dfrac{m' \circ e}{n \circ e} < g$ since $m' \notin A$, while $f < \dfrac{m' \circ e}{n \circ e}$ is a result of (2) ▲

Corollary

For any $f \in K$ there exist $r_1, r_2 \in R$ such that $r_1 < f < r_2$.

Proof The proof is immediate from the theorem and the fact that $f - e < f < f + e$ ▲

For any member f of the complete ordered field K, define two subsets of the rational subfield R by

$$(3) \qquad\qquad L_f = \{r: \ r \in R \text{ and } r \leq f\}$$

and

$$(4) \qquad\qquad U_f = \{r: \ r \in R \text{ and } f \leq r\}.$$

We call these, respectively, the *lower* and the *upper* set determined by f. The major result of this article shows that L_f and U_f each determines f.

Theorem 10

The quantities $\sup L_f$ and $\inf U_f$ exist, and each equals f.

Proof By the corollary to Theorem 9, L_f is not empty. Since the set is bounded above by f, $\sup L_f$ exists and $\sup L_f \leq f$. But if $\sup L_f < f$, then there is a member r of R such that $\sup L_f < r < f$ so that r is a member of L_f, yet it exceeds the supremum of that set. From this contradiction we conclude $\sup L_f = f$. The result $\inf U_f = f$ is proved similarly ▲

4 ISOMORPHISM OF COMPLETE ORDERED FIELDS

Two ordered fields F and F^* are *isomorphic* if there exists a one-to-one mapping φ from F onto F^* such that for $f,g \in F$

$$(5) \quad \begin{array}{ll} (a) & \varphi(f + g) = \varphi(f) + \varphi(g), \\ (b) & \varphi(fg) = \varphi(f)\varphi(g), \text{ and} \\ (c) & f \leq g \text{ if and only if } \varphi(f) \leq \varphi(g). \end{array}$$

In essence, this means that members of F and F^* are paired in such a way that matching elements behave identically with regard to addition, multiplication, and order.

As was stated earlier, the object of the present chapter is to prove that if K and K^* are complete ordered fields, then they are "intrinsically the same"; stated formally, we intend to prove that K and K^* are isomorphic. We shall do this after first establishing a comparable result for their rational subfields; it should be noted that this result does not require the hypothesis of completeness.

Theorem 11

Let R and R^* be the rational subfields of the ordered fields F and F^*, respectively. Then R and R^* are isomorphic.

Proof Let θ and θ^* be the zeros, and let e and e^* be the units of R and R^*, respectively. For each member $\dfrac{m \circ e}{n \circ e}$ of R, let

$$\varphi\left(\frac{m \circ e}{n \circ e}\right) = \frac{m \circ e^*}{n \circ e^*}.$$

In this manner a function φ is defined from R, and it is clear that the mapping is onto R^*. By Theorem 4, $\dfrac{m \circ e}{n \circ e} < \dfrac{p \circ e}{q \circ e}$ if and only if $mq < np$, and this is true if and only if $\dfrac{m \circ e^*}{n \circ e^*} < \dfrac{p \circ e^*}{q \circ e^*}$; thus $\dfrac{m \circ e}{n \circ e} < \dfrac{p \circ e}{q \circ e}$ if and only if $\varphi\left(\dfrac{m \circ e}{n \circ e}\right) < \varphi\left(\dfrac{p \circ e}{q \circ e}\right)$. This establishes the order-preserving character of the mapping and also shows it to be one-to-one.

Theorem 5 assures that sums are preserved by the mapping, for from this theorem follows

$$\varphi\left(\frac{m \circ e}{n \circ e} + \frac{p \circ e}{q \circ e}\right) = \varphi\left(\frac{(mq + np) \circ e}{nq \circ e}\right) = \frac{(mq + np) \circ e^*}{nq \circ e^*}$$

$$= \frac{m \circ e^*}{n \circ e^*} + \frac{p \circ e^*}{q \circ e^*} = \varphi\left(\frac{m \circ e}{n \circ e}\right) + \varphi\left(\frac{p \circ e}{q \circ e}\right).$$

Similarly, the preservation of products is implied by Theorem 6 ▲

Incidentally, it should be noted that in the above proof we established something stronger than statement (c) of (5); namely, if $r_1, r_2 \in R$, then

(6) $r_1 < r_2$ if and only if $\varphi(r_1) < \varphi(r_2)$.

Of course, this is also an immediate consequence of statement (c) and the one-to-one property of the mapping.

Theorem 12

The complete ordered fields K and K^* are isomorphic.

Proof   Take R and R^* to be the rational subfields of K and K^*, respectively.   Let φ be the mapping of Theorem 11 so that φ is defined from R onto R^*.   Our first task is to extend the domain of φ to all of K.

For any subset A of R, let $\varphi(A) = \{\varphi(r) \colon r \in A\}$; thus $\varphi(A)$ is a subset of R^*.   It can easily be seen from the one-to-one character of φ that, conversely, if A^* is any subset of R^*, then there is a unique $A \subset R$ with $\varphi(A) = A^*$.   In this way φ induces a one-to-one mapping $A \leftrightarrow \varphi(A)$ between the collection of subsets of R and those of R^*.

For $f \in K$, let L_f and U_f be the lower and upper sets defined by (3) and (4) of Article 3 so that $f = \sup L_f = \inf U_f$.   Clearly each member of $\varphi(L_f)$ is less than or equal to each member of $\varphi(U_f)$; from this follow the existence of sup $\varphi(L_f)$ and inf $\varphi(U_f)$ and the inequality

(7) $$\text{sup } \varphi(L_f) \leq \text{inf } \varphi(U_f).$$

In fact, as we next show, equality must prevail in (7).

Suppose that sup $\varphi(L_f) < $ inf $\varphi(U_f)$. Two applications of Theorem 9 assure the existence of members $\varphi(r_1)$ and $\varphi(r_2)$ of R^* with

$$\text{sup } \varphi(L_f) < \varphi(r_1) < \varphi(r_2) < \text{inf } \varphi(U_f).$$

Now if $s \in L_f$, then $\varphi(s) \in \varphi(L_f)$ so that $\varphi(s) < \varphi(r_1)$; hence $s < r_1$. From this it follows that $f = \text{sup } L_f \leq r_1$. In a similar way, $r_2 \leq$ inf $U_f = f$; by combining these results we have $r_1 = r_2$. However, this is a contradiction to the statement of (6), and so we are forced to the conclusion sup $\varphi(L_f) = $ inf $\varphi(U_f)$.

If f happens to be a member of R, then $f \in L_f$ and $f \in U_f$; in this event it is clear that

(8) $$\varphi(f) = \text{sup } \varphi(L_f) = \text{inf } \varphi(U_f).$$

If $f \notin R$, then define $\varphi(f)$ to be sup $\varphi(L_f) = $ inf $\varphi(U_f)$. In this manner the domain of φ is extended to all of K; moreover, from the way in which the extension is defined, (8) holds throughout.

To prove the order-preserving character of φ, consider $f,g \in K$ with $f < g$. Let $r_1,r_2 \in R$ satisfy $f < r_1 < r_2 < g$. Then $r_1 \in U_f$ so that $\varphi(r_1) \in \varphi(U_f)$, from which $\varphi(f) = $ inf $\varphi(U_f) \leq \varphi(r_1)$. Similarly, $r_2 \in L_g$ from which $\varphi(g) = $ sup $\varphi(L_g) \geq \varphi(r_2)$. Together these results yield

$$\varphi(f) \leq \varphi(r_1) < \varphi(r_2) \leq \varphi(g).$$

From this we conclude that φ is order-preserving and that φ is a one-to-one mapping from K onto its range.

As yet, we have not established the range of φ to be K^*; this we do next. Let $h^* \in K^*$, and consider the set $B = \{f \colon f \in K$ and $\varphi(f) \geq h^*\}$. By the corollary to Theorem 9, there are members $\varphi(r_1)$ and $\varphi(r_2)$ of R^* with $\varphi(r_1) < h^* < \varphi(r_2)$. Since r_2 is a member of B and r_1 a lower bound, we know that the infimum of B exists. Denoting this by g, we first assume $\varphi(g) < h^*$. Then some $\varphi(r) \in R^*$ can be found with $\varphi(g) < \varphi(r) < h^*$. This implies that r is a lower bound of B and that $g < r$, an impossibility. Next assume $h^* < \varphi(g)$ so that $h^* < \varphi(s) < \varphi(g)$ for some $\varphi(s) \in R^*$. Then $s \in B$ and $s < g$, which is also impossible. We conclude $\varphi(g) = h^*$; thus the range of φ is K^*.

To show that φ preserves sums, consider $f,g \in K$. For any $r,s \in R$ with $r \leq f$ and $s \leq g$ we have $r + s \leq f + g$ so that $\varphi(r) + \varphi(s) = \varphi(r + s) \leq \varphi(f + g)$. Thus $\varphi(r) \leq \varphi(f + g) - \varphi(s)$ for all $r \in L_f$, and this implies

$$(9) \qquad \varphi(f) = \sup \varphi(L_f) \leq \varphi(f + g) - \varphi(s).$$

Rearranging (9), we see that $\varphi(s) \leq \varphi(f + g) - \varphi(f)$ for all $s \leq g$. Hence

$$\varphi(g) = \sup \varphi(L_g) \leq \varphi(f + g) - \varphi(f)$$

or $\varphi(f) + \varphi(g) \leq \varphi(f + g)$. A similar argument using $\inf \varphi(U_f)$ and $\inf \varphi(U_g)$ leads to the reverse inequality, and we conclude $\varphi(f + g) = \varphi(f) + \varphi(g)$.

For use below we note a consequence of this last result; namely, $\varphi(-f) = -\varphi(f)$ for $f \in K$. This is immediate from $\varphi(f) + \varphi(-f) = \varphi(f - f) = \varphi(\theta) = \theta^*$.

We begin the proof that products are preserved by considering positive members f and g of K. For any $r,s \in R$ with $\theta < r \leq f$ and $\theta < s \leq g$, it follows from $rs \leq fg$ that $\varphi(r)\varphi(s) = \varphi(rs) \leq \varphi(fg)$. Reasoning like the above leads to $\varphi(f)\varphi(g) \leq \varphi(fg)$. Similarly, $\varphi(fg) \leq \varphi(f)\varphi(g)$; hence

$$(10) \qquad\qquad \varphi(fg) = \varphi(f)\varphi(g)$$

for f and g positive. If either f or g is zero, it is clear that

$$\varphi(fg) = \theta^* = \varphi(f)\varphi(g).$$

Suppose f and g are one positive and one negative; to be definite, take $f < \theta$ and $g > \theta$. Using the remark of the last paragraph,

$$\varphi(fg) = -\varphi((-f)g) = -\varphi(-f)\varphi(g) = \varphi(f)\varphi(g).$$

The case $f < \theta$ and $g < \theta$ is similar. Hence we conclude that (10) holds in all cases. This completes the proof that K and K^* are isomorphic ▲

EXERCISES AND EXTENSIONS

1. Establish that the subfield $\{n \circ e: \; n \in I\}$ of an ordered field F is isomorphic with the system of integers. Because of this, members of F of the form $n \circ e$ are called *integers.*

2. Prove that the rational subfield of any ordered field is countable.

3. For the system $\mathfrak{R}$ of Chapter 6, establish that the rational subfield is the set of those members of $\mathfrak{R}$ that are repeating. [See Exercises 13 and 14 of Chapter 6.]

A member of an ordered field is *rational* if it is a member of the rational subfield; otherwise it is *irrational.*

4. Prove that in the system $\mathfrak{R}$ of Chapter 6 the set of irrational numbers is not countable.

5. Let f be a rational and g an irrational member of an ordered field F. (*a*) Prove that $f + g$ is irrational. (*b*) Is fg irrational?

6. Produce examples to show that (*a*) the sum and (*b*) the product of two irrational numbers may be rational or may be irrational.

In the statements and proofs of the next exercises conventional notation is used for real numbers.

7. Prove that there is no rational number x such that $x^2 = 2$. [SUGGESTION: Let x be rational so that $x = p/q$ for integers p and q; by employing Exercise 37 of Chapter 5 it may be supposed that p and q have no common factors other than 1 and -1. Show that the assumption $x^2 = 2$ leads to a contradiction.]

8. The real number e, the base of the natural logarithms, is defined by $e = \displaystyle\sum_{n=0}^{\infty} \frac{1}{n!}.$ Prove that e is irrational. [SUGGESTION: Assume that $e = p/q$ for integers p and q. Then $c = q!\left(e - 1 - \dfrac{1}{1!} - \cdots - \dfrac{1}{q!}\right)$ is an integer. Arrive at the contradiction $0 < c < 1$ by expressing c as a series and comparing it with the geometric series $\displaystyle\sum_{n=1}^{\infty} \frac{1}{(q+1)^n}$.]

9. Prove that the set of irrational numbers is dense in $\mathfrak{R}$. [SUG-GESTION: From the density of rational numbers, for any real numbers a and b with $a < b$ there are rational numbers s and t such that $a < s < t < b$. Show that for a sufficiently large integer n, $s + \dfrac{\sqrt{2}}{n} < t$; verify that $s + \dfrac{\sqrt{2}}{n}$ is irrational.]

The remaining definitions and exercises pertain to a given ordered field F. Exercises 16 through 23 have to do with various properties of F that are equivalent to the completeness property $[F3]$. In order to formulate these statements, the definitions and facts that follow are needed.

For a given $a,b \in F$ with $a < b$, the set $[a,b] = \{x: \ x \in F, \ a \leq x \leq b\}$ is a *closed interval*, and $(a,b) = \{x: \ x \in F, \ a < x < b\}$ is an *open interval*. For any subset A of F, a point c is a *cluster point* of A if $J \cap A$ is an infinite set for each open interval J such that $c \in J$. A set A is *closed* if each cluster point of A is a member of A; a set B is *open* if B^c is closed.

10. (*a*) Prove that a finite subset of F is closed. (*b*) Prove that the sets F and $\varnothing$ are both closed and open.

11. Prove that c is a cluster point of a set A if and only if $A \cap [J - \{c\}] \neq \varnothing$ for each open interval J such that $c \in J$.

12. Establish the following: (*a*) The set A is closed if and only if for each $c \notin A$ there is an open interval J_c with $c \in J_c$ and $J_c \cap A = \varnothing$. (*b*) The set B is open if and only if for each $b \in B$ there is an open interval J_b with $b \in J_b$ and $J_b \subset B$.

13. Prove that (*a*) a closed interval is a closed set and (*b*) an open interval is an open set.

A collection $\mathcal{G}$ of subsets of F *covers* a set C if for each $x \in C$ there is some $G \in \mathcal{G}$ such that $x \in G$.

14. Show that a collection $\mathcal{G}$ of subsets covers C if and only if $C \subset \cup_{G \in \mathcal{G}} G$.

15. Let R be the rational subfield of the ordered field F, and let $\mathcal{G}$ be the collection of all intervals $(r - e, r + e)$ for $r \in R$. Prove that $\mathcal{G}$ covers F.

An ordered field F is *Archimedean* if for $a,b \in F$ with $0 < a < b$ there is an integer n such that $b < na$. A sequence $\{a_n\}$ of F is *increasing* (*decreasing*) if $a_n \leq a_{n+1}$ ($a_n \geq a_{n+1}$) for $n \in I_\omega$; it is *bounded* if the set $\{a_n : n \in I_\omega\}$ is bounded. The sequence $\{a_n\}$ *converges* to a *limit* $a \in F$ if, for each $\varepsilon \in F$ with $\varepsilon > 0$, there is an n_ε such that $|a_n - a| < \varepsilon$ for $n > n_\varepsilon$. We say that $\{a_n\}$ is a *Cauchy sequence* if, for each $\varepsilon \in F$ with $\varepsilon > 0$, there is an n_ε such that $|a_n - a_m| < \varepsilon$ for $n > n_\varepsilon$ and $m > n_\varepsilon$.

Following are various properties that an ordered field F may possess. Exercises 16 through 23 establish the equivalence of these properties; that is, these exercises establish that if an ordered field has any one of these properties, it has all of them.

Property 1. Any nonempty subset of F that is bounded above has a supremum.

Property 1'. Any nonempty subset of F that is bounded below has an infimum.

Property 2. [*Heine-Borel property*] If B is a closed bounded subset of F, and if $\mathcal{G}$ is a collection of open intervals that covers B, then there is a finite subset $\mathcal{G}_1$ of $\mathcal{G}$ that covers B.

Property 3. [*Bolzano-Weierstrass property*] If C is a bounded infinite subset of F, then the set of cluster points of C is not empty.

Property 4. (a) F is Archimedean and (b) [*nested intervals property*] if $\{A_n\}$ is a sequence of closed bounded intervals such that $A_{n+1} \subset A_n$ for $n \in I_\omega$, then $\bigcap_{n \in I_\omega} A_n$ is not empty.

Property 5. (a) F is Archimedean and (b) every bounded increasing sequence in F has a limit in F.

Property 5'. (a) F is Archimedean and (b) every bounded decreasing sequence in F has a limit in F.

Property 6. (a) F is Archimedean and (b) every Cauchy sequence in F has a limit in F.

16. Establish that Property 1 implies Property 1'.

17. Establish that Property 1' implies Property 2. [SUGGESTION: $B \subset [a,b]$ for some interval $[a,b]$. If $x \in B^c$, there is an open interval J_x such that $x \in J_x$ and $J_x \cap B = \varnothing$; hence $\mathsf{G}^* = \mathsf{G} \cup \{J_x: \ x \in B^c\}$ covers $[a,b]$. Let Y be the set of all $y \in [a,b]$ such that $[y,b]$ is covered by a finite subset of G^*. Prove that Y has an infimum y_0 and that $y_0 = a$; from this deduce Property 2.]

18. Establish that Property 2 implies Property 3. [SUGGESTION: Assume that C has no cluster points so that C is closed and bounded. Establish that for $x \in C$ there is an open interval J_x such that $x \in J_x$ and $J_x \cap C = \{x\}$. Use the fact that $\{J_x: \ x \in C\}$ covers C to establish Property 3.]

19. Establish that Property 3 implies Property 4. [SUGGESTION: (a) If F is not Archimedean, then $a,b \in F$ exist with $0 < a < b$ such that $a \le na < b$ for each positive integer n. Prove that $\{na: \ n \in I_+\}$ has no cluster points, and show that this leads to a contradiction. (b) Let $A_n = [a_n, b_n]$. The conclusion is immediate if $\{a_n: \ n \in I_\omega\}$ is finite; otherwise, show that $\{a_n: \ n \in I_\omega\}$ has a cluster point a and that $a \in A_n$ for all n.]

20. Establish that Property 4 implies Property 5. [SUGGESTION: Let $\{a_n\}$ be a bounded increasing sequence. For each n there is an integer m_n such that $c_n = a_n + \dfrac{m_n}{n}$ is an upper bound of the sequence while $c_n - \dfrac{1}{n}$ is not. Let $b_n = \min \{c_1, \ldots, c_n\}$; show that $[a_n, b_n]$ is a nested sequence and that $a \in \bigcap_{n \in I_\omega}[a_n, b_n]$ is a limit of $\{a_n\}$.]

21. Establish that Property 5 implies Property 5′.

22. Establish that Property 5′ implies Property 6. [SUGGESTION: Let $\{c_n\}$ be a Cauchy sequence. Then for each n there is an m_n such that $c_{m_n} - \dfrac{1}{n} < c_n < c_{m_n} + \dfrac{1}{n}$ for $n > m_n$. For each m let $N_m = \max \{m_n : 1 \leq n \leq m\}$ and $b_m = \min \left\{c_{m_n} + \dfrac{1}{n} : 1 \leq n \leq m\right\}$. Show that $\{b_m\}$ is decreasing and that $b_m - \dfrac{2}{m} < c_n < b_m$ for $n > N_m$. Then prove that the limit of $\{b_m\}$ is the limit of $\{c_n\}$.]

23. Establish that Property 6 implies Property 1. [SUGGESTION: Let a be a member of the set A and b an upper bound of A. Prove that for each n there is a k_n such that $a_n = a + \dfrac{k_n}{n}$ is an upper bound of A, but $a_n - \dfrac{1}{n}$ is not. Show that $|a_n - a_m| \leq \min \left\{\dfrac{1}{n}, \dfrac{1}{m}\right\}$ and deduce that $\{a_n\}$ is a Cauchy sequence. Then prove that the limit of this sequence is the supremum of A.]

Dedekind's Definition

Chapter Eight
Dedekind's Definition

1 RATIONAL NUMBERS

Having proved the existence and uniqueness of the real number system, we turn now to our second objective, which is to present the classical definitions of real numbers due to Dedekind and to Cantor. Since both of these are based on the system of rational numbers, we begin with a discussion of such quantities.

The *rational number system* is an ordered quadruple $(R, +, \cdot, \leq)$ consisting of a set R, operations $+$ and $\cdot$ on R, and a relation $\leq$ in R, which is such that

(1)   R1. $(R, +, \cdot, \leq)$ is an ordered field, and
       R2. $(R, +, \cdot, \leq)$ is isomorphic to its rational subfield.

It is easy to see from condition *R2* and from Theorem 11 of Chapter 7 that rational numbers are unique in the sense that two such systems must be isomorphic.

The existence of such a system has been established in the previous chapters. Indeed, the rational subfield of the real numbers, which in the notation of Chapter 7 consists of all members of the form $\dfrac{m \circ e}{n \circ e}$, satisfies requirements *R1* and *R2*; we shall take this as proof that the rational number system exists. It should be pointed out, however, that existence also can be established in an entirely different way—one that depends only on the system of integers and does not require the prior development of the real number system. This alternative proof, which involves ordered pairs of integers, is not difficult but is fairly lengthy. We omit the construction here since technically it is unnecessary; an outline of it is to be found in the Appendix.

We shall use the symbol R for the system as well as for the set of rational numbers. Since R is an ordered field, the statements of Chapter 5 pertaining to an ordered integral domain are all valid in R. Also, those properties of Chapter 7 that do not depend on completeness are possessed by the rational numbers.

The set I of integers may be placed in one-to-one correspondence with a subset of R by means of the mapping

$$\varphi(n) = n \circ e.$$

From the statements of (1) in Chapter 7, it is easy to see that this mapping is an isomorphism; that is,

$$\varphi(m + n) = \varphi(m) + \varphi(n),$$
$$\varphi(mn) = \varphi(m)\varphi(n), \text{ and}$$
$$m < n \text{ if and only if } \varphi(m) < \varphi(n).$$

Thus the subset $\{n \circ e: \ n \in I\}$ of R has all the attributes of the set of integers. For this reason, we shall henceforth use the symbol I also to denote the set $\{n \circ e: \ n \in I\}$, and members of R of the form $n \circ e$ will be referred to as *integers*. In addition, we shall adopt the usual convention and denote the zero and the unit of R simply by 0 and 1, respectively.

For $a \in R$ we define the *absolute value* $|a|$ by

$$(2) \qquad |a| = \begin{cases} a & \text{if } a \geq 0, \\ -a & \text{if } a < 0. \end{cases}$$

Then $0 \leq |a|$, $|a| = |-a|$, and $a \leq |a|$ are immediate.

Theorem 1

If $a, b \in R$, then

(a) $|ab| = |a|\,|b|$.
(b) $|a + b| \leq |a| + |b|$.

Proof (a) If $a < 0$ and $b \geq 0$, then

$$|ab| = -(ab) = (-a)b = |a|\,|b|.$$

This equality is established similarly for other cases. (b) $a \leq |a|$ and $b \leq |b|$, so that $a + b \leq |a| + |b|$. Also, $-a \leq |-a| = |a|$

and $-b \leq |b|$, so that $-(a + b) \leq |a| + |b|$.   The inequality then follows from the fact that $|a + b| = a + b$ or $|a + b| = -(a + b)$ ▲

From this can be established other properties, including the *triangle inequality*, part (a) of the next theorem.

Theorem 2

If $a,b,c \in R$, then

(a) $|a - b| \leq |a - c| + |b - c|$.

(b) $| |a| - |b| | \leq |a - b|$.

Proof

(a) $|a - b| = |(a - c) + (c - b)|$
$$\leq |a - c| + |c - b|$$
$$\leq |a - c| + |b - c|.$$

(b) $|a| = |b + (a - b)| \leq |b| + |a - b|$

so that
$$|a| - |b| \leq |a - b|.$$

Similarly,
$$-(|a| - |b|) = |b| - |a| \leq |b - a| = |a - b|$$ ▲

Example 1   There is no rational number whose square is 2.   For assume that the statement is false, let $\frac{m}{n}$ be a rational number such that $\left(\frac{m}{n}\right)^2 = 2$, and take m and n to be relatively prime integers, that is, to have no common factors exceeding 1.   Then $m^2 = 2n^2$, so that m^2 is even; hence m is even, so that $m = 2p$ for some integer p.   From this, $4p^2 = 2n^2$ or $2p^2 = n^2$, and the same argument applied to n shows that $n = 2q$ for some integer q.   But then m and n have a common factor 2 contrary to the assumption that these integers were relatively prime.

2   DEDEKIND CUTS

A *Dedekind cut*, or simply a *cut*, is a subset α of R such that

(3)
   (*a*) $\alpha \neq \varnothing$ and $\alpha^c \neq \varnothing$ (where $\alpha^c = R - \alpha$),

   (*b*) $r \in \alpha$, $s \in R$, and $r < s$ imply $s \in \alpha$, and

   (*c*) α does not have a minimum.

We let $\overline{\mathfrak{R}}$ denote the set of all cuts. It is our intention to introduce operations and an order relation and thereby to convert the set into the system of real numbers.

It is clear that for any member $r_0 \in R$ the set

$$\{r: \quad r \in R \text{ and } r > r_0\}$$

is a cut. This is called a *rational* cut *based on* r_0, while any member of $\overline{\mathfrak{R}}$ that is not of this form is termed an *irrational cut*. It can be seen that a cut is rational if and only if its complement has a maximum. Special instances of rational cuts are the *zero* cut θ and the *unit* cut δ which are defined by

$$\theta = \{r: \quad r \in R \text{ and } r > 0\}$$

and
$$\delta = \{r: \quad r \in R \text{ and } r > 1\}.$$

Example 2   It is clear that the set

$$\zeta = \{r: \quad r \in R, r \geq 0, \text{ and } r^2 > 2\}$$

satisfies requirements (*a*) and (*b*) of (3) for a cut. Given $r \in \zeta$, let

(4)
$$s = \frac{2r + 2}{r + 2}.$$

Then $s \geq 0$ and from

(5)
$$s^2 - 2 = \frac{2(r^2 - 2)}{(r + 2)^2}$$

and $r^2 > 2$ it follows that $s^2 > 2$; hence $s \in \zeta$. Since

(6)
$$s - r = \frac{2 - r^2}{r + 2},$$

it can be seen that $s < r$. This means that ζ does not have a minimum; therefore it is a cut.

To show that ζ is an irrational cut we must establish that ζ^c does not have a maximum. Let $r \in \zeta^c$ be such that $r \geq 0$. Since no rational number has its square equal to 2, it follows that $r^2 < 2$. Let s be defined by (4) so that both (5) and (6) remain valid. The first of these shows that $s^2 < 2$ while the second ensures that $r < s$. Hence s is a member of ζ^c and exceeds r. It follows that ζ^c has no maximum and that the cut is irrational.

For any cut α it is easy to see that $s \in \alpha^c$ and $r < s$ imply $r \in \alpha^c$. Also, if $s \in \alpha^c$ and $t \in \alpha$, then $s < t$. Although t must exceed s, it is always possible to choose such quantities as near one another as is desired; this we show next.

Theorem 3

For any cut α and for any positive rational number u there exist rational numbers s and t such that $s \in \alpha^c$, $t \in \alpha$, and $0 < t - s < u$.

Proof Select any member s_0 of α^c and any member t_0 of α. For $n \in I_\omega$, let

$$s_n = s_0 + \frac{nu}{2}.$$

By the principle of Archimedes there is some n such that $t_0 < s_n$. Hence the set

$$\{n: \ n \in I_\omega \text{ and } s_n \in \alpha\}$$

is not empty. Since it is bounded below by 0, the set has a minimum n', and clearly $n' > 0$. The numbers $s = s_{n'-1}$ and $t = s_{n'}$ satisfy the conclusion of the theorem ▲

3 ORDER

Equality of members of $\overline{\mathfrak{R}}$ has the usual meaning for sets; one consequence is the following.

Theorem 4

$\theta \neq \delta.$

Order in $\overline{\mathfrak{R}}$ is easily defined in terms of set inclusion. Thus for cuts α and β we write $\alpha \leq \beta$ if and only if $\beta \subset \alpha$.

Theorem 5

$\leq$ is a linear order.

Proof $\alpha \leq \alpha$ since $\alpha \subset \alpha$. Since $\beta \subset \alpha$ and $\gamma \subset \beta$ imply $\gamma \subset \alpha$, it follows that $\alpha \leq \beta$ and $\beta \leq \gamma$ imply $\alpha \leq \gamma$. Also, $\beta \subset \alpha$ and $\alpha \subset \beta$ imply $\alpha = \beta$; hence $\alpha \leq \beta$ and $\beta \leq \alpha$ imply $\alpha = \beta$. Thus the relation is an order.

To establish linearity of the order, suppose that $\alpha \neq \beta$. From this it may be assumed without loss of generality that there is some r such that $r \in \alpha$ and $r \notin \beta$, from which $r \in \beta^c$. If $s \in \beta$, then $r < s$ so that $s \in \alpha$; that is, $\beta \subset \alpha$, and from this it follows that $\alpha \leq \beta$ ▲

It also can be shown that $\overline{\mathfrak{R}}$ is complete.

Theorem 6

A nonempty subset of $\overline{\mathfrak{R}}$ that is bounded below has an infimum.

Proof Let B be a nonempty subset that is bounded below, and define the subset β_1 of R by

$$\beta_1 = \bigcup_{\beta \in B} \beta.$$

If α is a lower bound of B, then, for all $\beta \in B$, $\alpha \leq \beta$; hence $\beta \subset \alpha$. It follows that $\beta_1 \subset \alpha$ and $\alpha^c \subset \beta_1{}^c$, and from this we see that $\beta_1{}^c \neq \varnothing$. Since B is not empty, it is clear that $\beta_1 \neq \varnothing$.

Suppose that $r \in \beta_1$ and that $r < s$. Then, for some $\beta \in B$, $r \in \beta$ so that $s \in \beta$. Hence $s \in \beta_1$. Similarly, if $t \in \beta_1$, then $t \in \beta$ for some $\beta \in B$. But β is a cut, and so there is some $s \in \beta$ such that $s < t$; then $s \in \beta_1$, and it follows that β_1 has no minimum. From these various properties it can be seen that β_1 is a cut.

That β_1 is a lower bound of B is clear since $\beta \in B$ implies $\beta \subset \beta_1$ or $\beta_1 \leq \beta$. Finally, from the first paragraph it follows that $\alpha \leq \beta_1$ for any lower bound α of B ▲

4 ADDITION

The *sum* of members α and β of $\overline{\mathfrak{R}}$ is defined to be

(7) $$\alpha + \beta = \{r + s: \quad r \in \alpha \text{ and } s \in \beta\}.$$

Thus the sum of two cuts is the set of all sums of rational numbers that can be formed by adding a member of α to a member of β. It is necessary first of all to establish that $\alpha + \beta$ is indeed a cut.

Since both α and β are nonempty, it is clear that $\alpha + \beta$ is also. Let $r_1 \in \alpha^c$ and $s_1 \in \beta^c$, and suppose that $r_1 + s_1 \in \alpha + \beta$. Then for some $r_2 \in \alpha$ and some $s_2 \in \beta$,

$$r_1 + s_1 = r_2 + s_2.$$

But $r_1 < r_2$ and $s_1 < s_2$. Hence the preceding equation is impossible, and we conclude that $(\alpha + \beta)^c$ is not empty.

If $r \in \alpha$, $s \in \beta$, and $r + s < t$, then

(8) $$t = r + (t - r)$$

so that $s < t - r$. It follows that $t - r \in \beta$ and, from (8), that $t \in \alpha + \beta$. Thus $u \in \alpha + \beta$ and $u < t$ imply $t \in \alpha + \beta$.

Finally, if $r + s \in \alpha + \beta$ with $r \in \alpha$ and $s \in \beta$, then there is some $t \in \alpha$ with $t < r$. Thus $t + s \in \alpha + \beta$ and $t + s < r + s$, and it follows that $\alpha + \beta$ has no minimum. Combining the foregoing, we conclude that $\alpha + \beta$ is a cut.

Example 3 Let α and β be rational cuts based on a and b, respectively. If $r \in \alpha$ and $s \in \beta$, then $r + s > a + b$, from which it follows that $\alpha + \beta$ is not less than γ, the rational cut based on $a + b$. Conversely, if $t \in \gamma$ so that $t > a + b$, then $t = r + s$, where $r = \frac{1}{2}(t + a - b)$ and $s = \frac{1}{2}(t - a + b)$. Since $r > a$ and $s > b$, it follows that $t \in \alpha + \beta$; hence γ is not less than $\alpha + \beta$. Combining these results, we see that the sum of rational cuts based on a and b, respectively, is the rational cut based on $a + b$.

Theorem 7

$$\alpha + \beta = \beta + \alpha.$$

Theorem 8

$$\alpha + (\beta + \gamma) = (\alpha + \beta) + \gamma.$$

These statements are easy consequences of the definition of sum and the properties of rational numbers; proofs are omitted.

Theorem 9

$$\alpha + \theta = \alpha.$$

Proof Let $r \in \alpha + \theta$ so that $r = s + t$ for some $s \in \alpha$ and some $t \in \theta$. Then $s < s + t$ so that $s + t \in \alpha$. Hence $\alpha + \theta \subset \alpha$.

Next, suppose that $r \in \alpha$. Then there is some $s \in \alpha$ with $s < r$. Since $r = s + (r - s)$ and $r - s > 0$, it follows that $r \in \alpha + \theta$. Hence $\alpha \subset \alpha + \theta$ ▲

The *negative* $-\alpha$ of a cut α is defined to be the set of all rational numbers r such that $-r$ is in α^c but is not the maximum of that set if such a maximum exists; thus,

$$(9) \qquad -\alpha = \{r: \; -r \in \alpha^c \text{ and } -r \neq \max \alpha^c\}.$$

Since $\alpha \neq \varnothing$, there is some r which is a member of α, and it follows that $-r$ is not a member of $-\alpha$; hence $(-\alpha)^c \neq \varnothing$. Clearly α^c contains some member s which is not the largest in α^c [in fact, the set may have no largest member]; since $-s \in -\alpha$, it may be concluded that $-\alpha \neq \varnothing$. Suppose that $r \in -\alpha$ and $r < s$. Then $-r \in \alpha^c$ and $-s < -r$, so that $-s$ is a member of α^c but is not the largest in that set. Thus $s \in -\alpha$. Finally, to show that $-\alpha$ does not have a minimum, let $r \in -\alpha$ so that $-r \in \alpha^c$ and $-r \neq \max \alpha^c$. Then there is some $s \in \alpha^c$ with $-r < s$ and, from the fact that there are rational numbers lying between $-r$ and s, it may be assumed without loss of generality that s is not the maximum of α^c. From this follow $-s \in -\alpha$ and $-s < r$. Taken together, these statements show that the negative of a cut is itself a cut.

Theorem 10

$$\alpha + (-\alpha) = \theta.$$

Proof If $r \in \alpha$ and $s \in -\alpha$, then $-s \in \alpha^c$ so that $-s < r$. Hence $0 < r + s$ and $r + s \in \theta$. It follows that $\alpha + (-\alpha) \subset \theta$.

Let r be a member of θ so that $r > 0$. Then by Theorem 3 there exist rational numbers t_1 and t_2 satisfying $t_1 \in \alpha^c$, $t_2 \in \alpha$, and $0 < t_2 - t_1 < r$. We may assume that t_1 is not the largest member of α^c [otherwise t_1 could be replaced with $\frac{1}{2}(t_1 + t_2 - r)$]. Thus $-t_1 \in -\alpha$ so that $t_2 - t_1 \in \alpha + (-\alpha)$. But $t_2 - t_1 < r$ implies $r \in \alpha + (-\alpha)$; hence $\theta \subset \alpha + (-\alpha)$ ▲

Finally it can be seen that addition and order are compatible.

Theorem 11

$\alpha \leq \beta$ implies $\alpha + \gamma \leq \beta + \gamma$.

Proof If $\alpha \leq \beta$, then $\beta \subset \alpha$, from which $\beta + \gamma \subset \alpha + \gamma$; hence $\alpha + \gamma \leq \beta + \gamma$ ▲

At this stage, the facts reveal $(R, +, \leq)$ to be a linearly ordered commutative group; thus appropriate results of Chapter 5 are applicable.

5 MULTIPLICATION

The operation of multiplication is defined by starting with the set $\overline{\mathfrak{R}}' = \{\alpha: \alpha \geq \theta\}$ consisting of all nonnegative cuts. The *product* $\alpha\beta$ of members α and β of $\overline{\mathfrak{R}}'$ is defined to be the set

(10) $$\alpha\beta = \{rs: \ r \in \alpha \text{ and } s \in \beta\}.$$

Once more we must verify that the definition results in a cut. Clearly $\alpha\beta \neq \varnothing$, and the nonempty character of $(\alpha\beta)^c$ follows from the observation that all negative rational numbers are in that set. Suppose that $t \in \alpha\beta$ and $t < u$. Then $t = rs$ for some r and s with $r \in \alpha$ and $s \in \beta$. Since r is positive, $s < r^{-1}u$, implying that $r^{-1}u \in \beta$; hence $u = r(r^{-1}u)$ is a member of $\alpha\beta$. Finally, let $t \in \alpha\beta$ so that $t = rs$ for some $r \in \alpha$ and some $s \in \beta$. Then there exists a member u of α with $u < r$. Since us is a member of $\alpha\beta$ and since $us < rs$, it follows that $\alpha\beta$ has no least member. By combining these results we see that the product of nonnegative cuts is a cut.

Example 4 Let α and β be nonnegative rational cuts based on a and b, respectively; then a and b are nonnegative rational numbers. Let γ be the rational cut based on ab. If $r \in \alpha$ and $s \in \beta$, then $rs > ab$ so that $rs \in \gamma$. Hence $\gamma \leq \alpha\beta$. Conversely, let $t \in \gamma$ so that $ab < t$, and let $u = \min$ $\left\{1, \dfrac{t - ab}{a + b + 1}\right\}$. If $r = a + u$ and $s = b + u$, then $r \in \alpha,\ s \in \beta$, and

$$rs = ab + (a + b)u + u^2 \leq ab + (a + b + 1)u$$
$$\leq ab + (t - ab) = t.$$

Since rs is a member of $\alpha\beta$, so is t; hence $\alpha\beta \leq \gamma$. Thus the product of nonnegative rational cuts based on a and b, respectively, is the rational cut based on ab.

Commutativity and associativity are easily established, and we omit the proofs.

Theorem 12

$\alpha\beta = \beta\alpha$ for $\alpha, \beta \in \bar{\Re}'$.

Theorem 13

$\alpha(\beta\gamma) = (\alpha\beta)\gamma$ for $\alpha, \beta, \gamma \in \bar{\Re}'$.

Clearly δ is a member of $\bar{\Re}'$; we next show this to be the identity element for multiplication.

Theorem 14

$\alpha\delta = \alpha$ for $\alpha \in \bar{\Re}'$.

Proof If $r \in \alpha$ and $s \in \delta$, then $r < rs$ so that $rs \in \alpha$. Hence $\alpha\delta \subset \alpha$. On the other hand, if $r \in \alpha$, there is some $u \in \alpha$ with $u < r$. Since α is nonnegative, u is positive; therefore u^{-1} exists.

From $1 < ru^{-1}$ it follows that $ru^{-1} \in \delta$, and from $r = u(ru^{-1})$ it can be seen that $r \in \alpha\delta$. Hence $\alpha \subset \alpha\delta$ ▲

The next two theorems establish that multiplication interacts properly with addition and order.

Theorem 15

$\alpha(\beta + \gamma) = \alpha\beta + \alpha\gamma$ for $\alpha,\beta,\gamma \in \bar{\mathfrak{R}}'$.

Proof If $r \in \alpha\beta + \alpha\gamma$, then $r = st + uv$ for some s, t, u, and v with $s,u \in \alpha$, $t \in \beta$, and $v \in \gamma$. Without loss of generality, assume that $s \leq u$. Clearly $s(t + v)$ is a member of $\alpha(\beta + \gamma)$, and, since $r \geq s(t + v)$, so is r. Thus $\alpha\beta + \alpha\gamma \subset \alpha(\beta + \gamma)$.

The reverse set inclusion is easy to verify. For if $r \in \alpha(\beta + \gamma)$ so that $r = s(t + v)$ for some $s \in \alpha$, some $t \in \beta$, and some $v \in \gamma$, then $r = st + sv$ is a member of $\alpha\beta + \alpha\gamma$; hence $\alpha(\beta + \gamma) \subset \alpha\beta + \alpha\gamma$ ▲

Theorem 16

$\alpha \leq \beta$ implies $\alpha\gamma \leq \beta\gamma$ for $\alpha,\beta,\gamma \in \bar{\mathfrak{R}}'$.

Proof If $\alpha \leq \beta$, then $\beta \subset \alpha$ so that $\beta\gamma \subset \alpha\gamma$; hence $\alpha\gamma \leq \beta\gamma$ ▲

At this point we make an observation concerning a positive cut. If $\alpha > \theta$, then α is a proper subset of θ. That is, there is some rational number r that is a member of θ but not of α. Thus $r \in \alpha^c$, and it may be assumed without loss of generality that r is not the maximum of α^c if that set has a maximum [for otherwise r could be replaced with $\dfrac{r}{2}$]. The number r is positive since all members of θ have this property. In short, if $\alpha > \theta$, there is some r such that $r > 0$, $r \in \alpha^c$, and $r \neq \max \alpha^c$.

The *inverse* α^{-1} of a positive cut α is defined to be the set

(11) $\alpha^{-1} = \{r:\ r > 0,\ r^{-1} \in \alpha^c,\ \text{and}\ r^{-1} \neq \max \alpha^c\}$.

[Of course, α^c may not have a maximum, in which case the last condition is automatically satisfied.] The remarks of the preceding paragraph show that α^{-1} is not empty, and $(\alpha^{-1})^c$ is not empty since it must contain at least the negative rational numbers. Next, suppose that $r \in \alpha^{-1}$ and $r < s$. Then $r^{-1} \in \alpha^c$ and $s^{-1} < r^{-1}$ so that $s^{-1} \in \alpha^c$ too. Since s^{-1} is positive and is not the maximum of α^c, it follows that $s \in \alpha^{-1}$. Finally, if $t \in \alpha^{-1}$, then $t^{-1} \in \alpha^c$ and is not the maximum of that set. Hence there is some $u \in \alpha^c$ with $t^{-1} < u$, and we may select u so that it is not the maximum of α^c. Thus $u^{-1} \in \alpha^{-1}$ and, since $u^{-1} < t$, it follows that α^{-1} does not have a least member. We conclude that the inverse of a positive cut is a cut.

Theorem 17

$$\alpha\alpha^{-1} = \delta \text{ for any } \alpha > \theta.$$

Proof   Clearly the inverse of a positive cut is itself in $\bar{\Re}'$; hence the product $\alpha\alpha^{-1}$ is defined. If $r \in \alpha$ and $s \in \alpha^{-1}$, then $s^{-1} \in \alpha^c$ so that $s^{-1} < r$. Thus $1 < rs$, and it follows that $\alpha\alpha^{-1} \subset \delta$.

Next, consider any $r \in \delta$ so that $1 < r$. Let t_3 be a member of α^c such that $t_3 > 0$ and $t_3 \neq \max \alpha^c$. Then, by the principle of Archimedes, there is some positive integer n such that

$$t_3^{-1} < n(r - 1).$$

Employing Theorem 3, we may select $t_1 \in \alpha^c$ and $t_2 \in \alpha$ so that

$$0 < t_2 - t_1 < \frac{1}{n}.$$

It is clear that this may be done in such a way that $t_3 \leq t_1$ and $t_1 \neq \max \alpha^c$. Then $t_1 \in \alpha^{-1}$ and

$$t_2 t_1^{-1} < \left(t_1 + \frac{1}{n}\right) t_1^{-1} = 1 + \frac{1}{n} t_1^{-1}$$

$$\leq 1 + \frac{1}{n} t_3^{-1} < r.$$

Since $t_2 t_1^{-1} \in \alpha\alpha^{-1}$, it follows that $r \in \alpha\alpha^{-1}$. Hence $\delta \subset \alpha\alpha^{-1}$ ▲

Having defined multiplication on the set of nonnegative cuts, we now extend the operation to all of $\bar{\Re}$ just as was done in Article 8 of Chapter 6. Also, the inverse α^{-1} of a negative cut α

is defined to be $-(-\alpha)^{-1}$. It is easy to see that the various results of Chapter 6, Article 8, carry over immediately to the system $\bar{\mathfrak{R}}$. It follows that $\bar{\mathfrak{R}}$ is a complete ordered field; hence the definition of real numbers as the system of cuts is equivalent to the definition given in Chapter 6. The set of rational cuts is the rational subfield of $\bar{\mathfrak{R}}$ and, by Theorem 11 of Chapter 7, is isomorphic to the set of rational numbers. The irrational cuts are the irrational numbers.

EXERCISES AND EXTENSIONS

1. Develop the rational number system from the system of integers by supplying the details for the construction outlined in the Appendix.

2. Establish that the set of rational cuts is the rational subfield of $\bar{\mathfrak{R}}$.

3. Prove that $\xi = \{r:\ r \in R,\ r \geq 0,\ r^2 > 3\}$ is an irrational cut.

4. Verify that the cut ζ of Example 2 is such that $\zeta^2\,[= \zeta\zeta]$ is the rational cut based on 2.

5. With ζ as defined in Example 2 and ξ as defined in Exercise 3, show that (*a*) $\zeta\xi$ and (*b*) $\zeta + \xi$ are irrational cuts.

6. The systems $\mathfrak{R}$ of Chapter 6 and $\bar{\mathfrak{R}}$ of Chapter 8 are isomorphic because of the results of Chapter 7. Establish this directly by defining an isomorphic mapping from $\mathfrak{R}$ onto $\bar{\mathfrak{R}}$.

The *extended real number system* consists of the real numbers together with two elements ∞ and $-\infty$. These elements are such that the following statements are valid for any real number x.

$$-\infty < x < \infty,$$

$$\infty + \infty = x + \infty = \infty + x = \infty,$$

$$(-\infty) + (-\infty) = x + (-\infty)$$
$$= (-\infty) + x = -\infty,$$

$$(\infty)(\infty) = (-\infty)(-\infty) = \infty,$$

$$(\infty)(-\infty) = (-\infty)(\infty) = -\infty,$$

$$\infty x = x\infty = \begin{cases} \infty & \text{if } x > 0, \\ -\infty & \text{if } x < 0, \end{cases}$$

$$(-\infty)x = x(-\infty) = \begin{cases} -\infty & \text{if } x > 0, \\ \infty & \text{if } x < 0, \end{cases}$$

$$\frac{x}{\infty} = \frac{x}{-\infty} = 0.$$

7. Show that it is not possible to define $\infty - \infty$ in a manner that is consistent with the above rules and the usual associative, commutative, and distributive laws. Also show that it is not possible to define $0 \cdot \infty$.

8. Modify the definition of Dedekind cut by dropping condition (a) of (3) to the effect that $\alpha \neq \emptyset$ and $\alpha^c \neq \emptyset$. The resulting *extended collection of cuts* $\bar{\mathfrak{R}}^*$ includes the sets $R \ [= -\infty]$ and $\emptyset \ [= \infty]$. Examine the various definitions and theorems of this chapter and make necessary modifications so that the system that results is the extended real number system.

Cantor's Definition

Chapter Nine
Cantor's Definition

1 CAUCHY SEQUENCES

As before, we let R be the set of rational numbers and let I_ω be the set of nonnegative integers. A function defined on I_ω with range in R is called a *sequence* and is denoted by $\{a_n\}$, where a_n is the function value at n for each n in I_ω. A sequence $\{a_n\}$ is said to satisfy the *Cauchy condition* or to be a *Cauchy sequence* if, for any positive rational number ε, there is a rational number N such that

$$(1) \qquad\qquad |a_n - a_m| < \varepsilon$$

for all $n,m \in I_\omega$ with $n > N$ and $m > N$. The set of all Cauchy sequences will be denoted by S; this collection is the foundation for the Cantor definition of a real number.

A *constant* sequence is a sequence $\{a_n\}$ such that $a_n = a_0$ for all $n \in I_\omega$. It is easy to see that all such sequences are members of S. More generally, a sequence $\{b_n\}$ is in S if it *converges;* that is, if there is some rational number b such that, for any positive rational number ε, there is a rational number N with the property that

$$|b_n - b| < \varepsilon$$

for all $n \in I_\omega$ with $n > N$. Since we shall have no occasion to use this fact, its proof is left to the reader. It is important, however, to realize that convergence is not a necessary condition for membership in S. This, too, we shall not prove; however, it can be established by showing that the sequence

$$1.4, \ 1.41, \ 1.414, \ 1.4142, \ 1.41421, \ 1.414214, \ . \ . \ .$$

is a Cauchy sequence but does not converge *in the rational number system* since $\sqrt{2}$ is not a rational number.

Example 1 Consider the sequence $\{a_n\}$ with $a_0 = 0$, $a_1 = 1$, and

$$a_n = \tfrac{1}{2}(a_{n-1} + a_{n-2})$$

for $n \geq 2$. It is easy to establish by induction that

$$|a_{n+1} - a_n| = \frac{1}{2^n}$$

for $n \geq 0$ and that a_m lies between a_n and a_{n+1} if $m > n$. Hence

$$|a_m - a_n| \leq \frac{1}{2^n}$$

for $m > n$. From this it readily follows that the sequence satisfies the Cauchy condition.

A sequence $\{a_n\}$ is *bounded* if there is a rational number M such that

(2) $$|a_n| \leq M$$

for all $n \in I_\omega$. All the sequences we shall encounter will be of this type.

Theorem 1

Every Cauchy sequence is bounded.

Proof Let $\{a_n\}$ be a Cauchy sequence, and let N be such that

$$|a_n - a_m| < 1$$

for $n > N$ and $m > N$. Select a member n' of I_ω that exceeds N. Then for $n \geq n'$,

$$|a_n| \leq |a_{n'}| + |a_n - a_{n'}| < |a_{n'}| + 1.$$

Take M to be the maximum of the quantities

$$|a_0|, |a_1|, \ldots, |a_{n'-1}|, |a_{n'}| + 1.$$

Then $|a_n| \leq M$ for all n ▲

The symbol $\{a_n + b_n\}$ signifies a sequence whose function value at n is $a_n + b_n$. This is called the *sum* of $\{a_n\}$ and $\{b_n\}$.

Likewise the *difference* $\{a_n - b_n\}$, *negative* $\{-b_n\}$, and *product* $\{a_n b_n\}$ have obvious pointwise definitions.

Theorem 2

If $\{a_n\}$ and $\{b_n\}$ are Cauchy sequences, then so are $\{a_n + b_n\}$ and $\{a_n b_n\}$.

Proof Assume that $\{a_n\}$ and $\{b_n\}$ are Cauchy sequences. Then there is some M such that $M \geq 1$ and

$$|a_n| \leq M \qquad \text{and} \qquad |b_n| \leq M$$

for all $n \in I_\omega$. Also, for any $\varepsilon > 0$, there is an N such that

$$|a_n - a_m| < \frac{\varepsilon}{2M} \qquad \text{and} \qquad |b_n - b_m| < \frac{\varepsilon}{2M}$$

for $n > N$ and $m > N$. For such n and m it follows that

$$|(a_n + b_n) - (a_m + b_m)| \leq |a_n - a_m| + |b_n - b_m|$$

$$< 2\left(\frac{\varepsilon}{2M}\right) \leq \varepsilon.$$

Also

$$|a_n b_n - a_m b_m| = |a_n(b_n - b_m) + b_m(a_n - a_m)|$$

$$\leq |a_n|\,|b_n - b_m| + |b_m|\,|a_n - a_m|$$

$$< M\left(\frac{\varepsilon}{2M}\right) + M\left(\frac{\varepsilon}{2M}\right) = \varepsilon \;\blacktriangle$$

Corollary

If $\{a_n\}$ and $\{b_n\}$ are Cauchy sequences, then so are $\{-b_n\}$ and $\{a_n - b_n\}$.

Proof The sequence $\{c_n\}$ with $c_n = -1$ for all n is a Cauchy sequence; hence so is $\{c_n b_n\} = \{-b_n\}$. Therefore so is $\{a_n + (-b_n)\} = \{a_n - b_n\}$ ▲

We define a relation $\sim$ on $\mathcal{S}$ by stipulating that $\{a_n\} \sim \{b_n\}$ if and only if $\{a_n - b_n\}$ *converges to* 0; that is, for any $\varepsilon > 0$ there is an N such that

(3)
$$|a_n - b_n| < \varepsilon$$

for all $n \in I_\omega$ with $n > N$.

Theorem 3

$\sim$ is an equivalence relation on S.

Proof It is obvious that the relation is reflexive and symmetric. To prove it transitive, assume that

$$\{a_n\} \sim \{b_n\} \qquad \text{and} \qquad \{b_n\} \sim \{c_n\}.$$

Then, for any $\varepsilon > 0$, there is an N such that

$$|a_n - b_n| < \frac{\varepsilon}{2} \qquad \text{and} \qquad |b_n - c_n| < \frac{\varepsilon}{2}$$

for $n > N$. For such n

$$|a_n - c_n| \leq |a_n - b_n| + |b_n - c_n| < \varepsilon \; \blacktriangle$$

Example 2 The sequences $\left\{\dfrac{n^2}{n^2 + 2}\right\}$ and $\left\{\dfrac{n^4 + 4}{n^4 - 4}\right\}$ are equivalent since their difference $\left\{\dfrac{2}{n^2 - 2}\right\}$ converges to zero. Also, the sequences $\left\{\dfrac{1}{n}\right\}$ and $\left\{\dfrac{(-1)^n}{n}\right\}$ are equivalent.

Each Cauchy sequence $\{a_n\}$ determines an equivalence class consisting of all sequences equivalent to $\{a_n\}$; that is,

(4)
$$\{\{b_n\}: \quad \{b_n\} \in S \text{ and } \{b_n\} \sim \{a_n\}\}.$$

Example 3 Let $\{a_n\}$ be a sequence that converges to a and let $\{b_n\}$ be any member of S. Since $\{a_n - b_n\}$ converges to 0 if and only if $\{b_n\}$ converges to a, it follows that the equivalence class determined by $\{a_n\}$ is just the set of those sequences that converge to a. By the same token it can be seen that for any equivalence class either all members of the class converge [and to the same rational number] or none converges.

The collection of all equivalence classes of S will be denoted by $\widetilde{\mathfrak{R}}$, and members of $\widetilde{\mathfrak{R}}$ by α, β, and the like. Each Cauchy sequence belongs to one and only one equivalence class. In particular, the constant sequence $\{0\}$ is a member of an equivalence class which we shall call *zero* and signify by θ. The *unit* δ is the class to which the constant sequence $\{1\}$ belongs.

Theorem 4

$\theta \neq \delta$.

2 ADDITION

In converting $\widetilde{\mathfrak{R}}$ into the system of real numbers, we depart from prior practice and define arithmetic operations before the order relation. We begin with addition.

Theorem 5

If $\{a_n\} \sim \{b_n\}$ and $\{c_n\} \sim \{d_n\}$, then

$$\{-a_n\} \sim \{-b_n\}$$

and

$$\{a_n + c_n\} \sim \{b_n + d_n\}.$$

Proof Corresponding to $\varepsilon > 0$ there is an N such that

$$|a_n - b_n| < \frac{\varepsilon}{2} \quad \text{and} \quad |c_n - d_n| < \frac{\varepsilon}{2}$$

for $n > N$. Hence, for such n,

$$|(-a_n) - (-b_n)| = |a_n - b_n| < \varepsilon$$

and

$$|(a_n + c_n) - (b_n + d_n)| \leq |a_n - b_n| + |c_n - d_n| < \varepsilon \; \blacktriangle$$

Let α and β be members of $\widetilde{\mathfrak{R}}$ and suppose that $\{a_n\} \in \alpha$ and $\{b_n\} \in \beta$. The *sum* $\alpha + \beta$ of α and β is defined to be the member of $\widetilde{\mathfrak{R}}$ which contains the Cauchy sequence $\{a_n + b_n\}$. According to the preceding theorem, the class $\alpha + \beta$ does not depend on the particular sequences $\{a_n\}$ and $\{b_n\}$ employed; that is, the sum of two classes is independent of the *representatives* of those classes that are used in the definition.

Since $\{a_n + b_n\} = \{b_n + a_n\}$ and $\{a_n + (b_n + c_n)\} = \{(a_n + b_n) + c_n\}$, it can be seen at once that addition is commutative and associative.

Theorem 6

$$\alpha + \beta = \beta + \alpha.$$

Theorem 7

$$\alpha + (\beta + \gamma) = (\alpha + \beta) + \gamma.$$

As is to be expected, θ is the identity element for addition.

Theorem 8

$$\alpha + \theta = \alpha.$$

Proof Let $\{a_n\} \in \alpha$, and take the constant sequence $\{0\}$ as the representative of θ. Since $\{a_n + 0\} = \{a_n\}$ is a member of α, it follows that $\alpha + \theta = \alpha$ ▲

Consider any equivalence class α and let $\{a_n\}$ be a member of α. The *negative* $-\alpha$ of α is the class containing $\{-a_n\}$. By using Theorem 5, we see that this definition, too, is independent of the representative employed.

Theorem 9

$$\alpha + (-\alpha) = \theta.$$

Proof If $\{a_n\} \in \alpha$, then $\{-a_n\} \in -\alpha$; hence $\alpha + (-\alpha)$ is the equivalence class that contains $\{a_n + (-a_n)\} = \{0\}$ ▲

3   MULTIPLICATION

In the earlier schemes for constructing real numbers, we first defined multiplication for nonnegative elements and then extended the definition to include all others. In the present construction there is no need for this two-stage development.

Theorem 10

If $\{a_n\} \sim \{b_n\}$ and $\{c_n\} \sim \{d_n\}$, then

$$\{a_n c_n\} \sim \{b_n d_n\}.$$

Proof   Since $\{a_n\}$ and $\{d_n\}$ are bounded, there is some $M > 0$ such that

$$|a_n| \leq M \quad \text{and} \quad |d_n| \leq M.$$

Let $\varepsilon > 0$ be given. Then there is an N such that for $n > N$

$$|a_n - b_n| < \frac{\varepsilon}{2M} \quad \text{and} \quad |c_n - d_n| < \frac{\varepsilon}{2M}.$$

Hence, for such n,

$$
\begin{aligned}
|a_n c_n - b_n d_n| &= |a_n(c_n - d_n) + d_n(a_n - b_n)| \\
&\leq |a_n|\,|c_n - d_n| + |d_n|\,|a_n - b_n| \\
&< M\left(\frac{\varepsilon}{2M}\right) + M\left(\frac{\varepsilon}{2M}\right) = \varepsilon \;\blacktriangle
\end{aligned}
$$

For $\alpha,\ \beta \in \widetilde{\mathfrak{R}}$, let $\{a_n\} \in \alpha$ and $\{b_n\} \in \beta$. The *product* $\alpha\beta$ of α and β is the equivalence class to which $\{a_n b_n\}$ belongs. Because of Theorem 10, the product is well-defined.

Theorem 11

$$\alpha\beta = \beta\alpha.$$

Theorem 12

$$\alpha(\beta\gamma) = (\alpha\beta)\gamma.$$

Theorem 13

$\alpha\delta = \alpha$.

Theorem 14

$\alpha(\beta + \gamma) = \alpha\beta + \alpha\gamma$.

Theorems 11, 12, and 14 are immediate from the commutative, associative, and distributive laws for rational numbers. The proof of Theorem 13 parallels the proof that $\alpha + \theta = \alpha$.

Before defining an inverse, we must determine some additional properties of Cauchy sequences.

Theorem 15

Let $\{a_n\} \in S$ have the property that for any $\varepsilon > 0$ and any N there exists an n' such that $n' > N$ and $|a_{n'}| < \varepsilon$. Then $\{a_n\} \in \theta$.

Proof For $\varepsilon > 0$ there is some N such that

$$|a_n - a_m| < \frac{\varepsilon}{2}$$

for n and m exceeding N. Let $n' > N$ be such that

$$|a_{n'}| < \frac{\varepsilon}{2}.$$

Then for $n > n'$

$$|a_n - 0| = |a_n| \leq |a_n - a_{n'}| + |a_{n'}| < \varepsilon.$$

It follows that $\{a_n\} \sim \{0\}$ ▲

Corollary

If $\{a_n\} \notin \theta$, then there exists an $\varepsilon > 0$ and an N such that $|a_n| \geq \varepsilon$ for all $n > N$.

Theorem 16

Let $\{a_n\} \in S$ be such that $\{a_n\} \notin \theta$ and, for all n, $a_n \neq 0$. Then $\{a_n^{-1}\} \in S$.

Proof [The restriction $a_n \neq 0$ is needed, of course, to ensure that a_n^{-1} is defined.] By the corollary to Theorem 15, there exists a positive number k and an N_1 such that $|a_n| \geq k$ for all $n > N_1$. Also, for any $\varepsilon > 0$, there is an N_2 such that

$$|a_n - a_m| < k^2\varepsilon$$

for n and m exceeding N_2. Let $N = \max\{N_1, N_2\}$. Then for $n > N$ and $m > N$

$$|a_n^{-1} - a_m^{-1}| = \left| \frac{a_m - a_n}{a_n a_m} \right|$$

$$= \frac{|a_m - a_n|}{|a_n|\,|a_m|}$$

$$< \frac{k^2\varepsilon}{(k)(k)} = \varepsilon \ \blacktriangle$$

Consider an equivalence class α that is not equal to θ. If $\{a_n\} \in \alpha$, then there is some $k > 0$ and some N such that $|a_n| \geq k$ for $n > N$. Define a new sequence $\{b_n\}$ by

$$(5) \qquad\qquad b_n = \begin{cases} k & \text{if } n \leq N \\ a_n & \text{if } n > N. \end{cases}$$

It is easy to see that $\{b_n\}$ is a Cauchy sequence and, moreover, that $\{b_n\} \sim \{a_n\}$ so that $\{b_n\} \in \alpha$. Since, for all n, $b_n \neq 0$, it follows from the preceding theorem that $\{b_n^{-1}\}$ is a Cauchy sequence. The equivalence class of which $\{b_n^{-1}\}$ is a member is called the *inverse* of the class α and is denoted by α^{-1}.

We must prove that the inverse of α does not depend on the representative used in the definition. This will follow from the next theorem.

Theorem 17

Let $\{b_n\}$ and $\{c_n\}$ be members of an equivalence class α with $\alpha \neq \theta$, and assume that, for all n, $b_n \neq 0$ and $c_n \neq 0$. Then $\{b_n^{-1}\} \sim \{c_n^{-1}\}$.

Proof From the corollary to Theorem 15 it can be seen that there is a positive number k and an N_1 such that

$$k \leq |b_n| \qquad \text{and} \qquad k \leq |c_n|$$

for all $n > N_1$. Also, for any $\varepsilon > 0$, there is an N_2 such that

$$|b_n - c_n| < k^2 \varepsilon$$

for $n > N_2$. If $N = \max \{N_1, N_2\}$, then for $n > N$

$$|b_n^{-1} - c_n^{-1}| = \left| \frac{c_n - b_n}{b_n c_n} \right|$$

$$= \frac{|c_n - b_n|}{|b_n| \, |c_n|}$$

$$< \frac{k^2 \varepsilon}{(k)(k)} = \varepsilon \; \blacktriangle$$

Finally, we establish the basic property for an inverse.

Theorem 18

If $\alpha \neq \theta$, then $\alpha \alpha^{-1} = \delta$.

Proof Let $\{b_n\} \in \alpha$ be such that $\{b_n^{-1}\}$ exists. Then $\{b_n b_n^{-1}\} = \{1\}$ is a member of $\alpha \alpha^{-1}$; hence $\alpha \alpha^{-1} = \delta \; \blacktriangle$

4 ORDER

A Cauchy sequence $\{a_n\}$ is *nonnegative* if for any $\varepsilon > 0$ there is an N such that

$$(6) \qquad\qquad -\varepsilon < a_n$$

for all $n > N$. We let S' denote the set of such nonnegative sequences. It is easy to see that each member of θ is a member of S'. In the next few theorems we shall establish basic properties of nonnegative sequences. Following that, these sequences will be used to define an order relation in $\widetilde{\mathfrak{R}}$.

Theorem 19

If $\{a_n\}$ is a Cauchy sequence, then $\{a_n\} \in S'$ or $\{-a_n\} \in S'$.

Proof Assume that neither $\{a_n\}$ nor $\{-a_n\}$ is a member of S'. Then there is some $\varepsilon > 0$ such that for any N there exist integers

n and m that exceed N and for which

$$a_n \leq -\varepsilon \qquad \text{and} \qquad -a_m \leq -\varepsilon.$$

It follows that

$$|a_n - a_m| \geq 2\varepsilon,$$

contrary to the fact that $\{a_n\}$ is a Cauchy sequence ▲

Theorem 20

If $\{a_n\} \in S'$ and $\{-a_n\} \in S'$, then $\{a_n\} \in \theta$.

Proof If both $\{a_n\}$ and $\{-a_n\}$ are nonnegative, then, for any $\varepsilon > 0$, there is an N such that

$$-\varepsilon < a_n \qquad \text{and} \qquad -\varepsilon < -a_n$$

or, what is the same,

$$|a_n| < \varepsilon$$

for $n > N$ ▲

Theorem 21

If $\{a_n\} \in S'$ and $\{a_n\} \sim \{b_n\}$, then $\{b_n\} \in S'$.

Proof For any $\varepsilon > 0$ there exists an N such that

$$-\frac{\varepsilon}{2} < a_n$$

and

$$|a_n - b_n| < \frac{\varepsilon}{2}$$

for all $n > N$. Thus, for such n,

$$-\frac{\varepsilon}{2} < b_n - a_n$$

so that

$$-\varepsilon = -\frac{\varepsilon}{2} - \frac{\varepsilon}{2} < a_n + (b_n - a_n) = b_n \;▲$$

Theorem 22

If both $\{a_n\}$ and $\{b_n\}$ are nonnegative, then so are $\{a_n + b_n\}$ and $\{a_n b_n\}$.

Proof Since Cauchy sequences are bounded, there is some M such that

$$|a_n| \leq M \quad \text{and} \quad |b_n| \leq M$$

for all n, and, without loss of generality, we may assume that $M \geq 2$. For any $\varepsilon > 0$ there is an N such that

$$-\frac{\varepsilon}{M} < a_n \quad \text{and} \quad -\frac{\varepsilon}{M} < b_n$$

for all $n > N$. Hence, for such n,

$$-\varepsilon \leq -\frac{2\varepsilon}{M} < a_n + b_n,$$

which proves that the sum is nonnegative. As for the product, if a_n and b_n are both negative or both nonnegative, then $0 \leq a_n b_n$. If $a_n < 0$ and $b_n \geq 0$, then

$$-\varepsilon \leq \left(\frac{-\varepsilon}{M} \right) b_n < a_n b_n,$$

and a similar result follows in case $b_n < 0$ and $a_n \geq 0$. Thus, in any event,

$$-\varepsilon < a_n b_n$$

for all $n > N$ ▲

Let α and β be any equivalence classes and assume that $\{a_n\} \in \alpha$ and $\{b_n\} \in \beta$. We define the relation $\leq$ by stating that $\alpha \leq \beta$ if and only if $\{b_n - a_n\}$ is nonnegative. Because of the preceding theorem and the properties of addition for equivalence classes it can be seen that this definition does not depend on the representatives selected.

Theorem 23

The relation $\leq$ is a linear order on $\widetilde{\mathfrak{R}}$.

Proof The relation is reflexive, for if $\{a_n\} \in \alpha$, then $\{a_n - a_n\} = \{0\}$ is nonnegative so that $\alpha \leq \alpha$. Next, assume that $\alpha \leq \beta$ and $\beta \leq \alpha$, and let $\{a_n\} \in \alpha$ and $\{b_n\} \in \beta$. Then both $\{b_n - a_n\}$ and $\{a_n - b_n\}$ are nonnegative so that $\{b_n - a_n\} \in \theta$ by Theorem 20. That is, $\beta - \alpha = \theta$; hence $\alpha = \beta$. It follows that the relation is antisymmetric. Assume that $\alpha \leq \beta$ and $\beta \leq \gamma$; let $\{a_n\} \in \alpha$, $\{b_n\} \in \beta$, and $\{c_n\} \in \gamma$. Then $\{b_n - a_n\}$ and $\{c_n - b_n\}$ are non-negative; hence so is $\{(c_n - b_n) + (b_n - a_n\} = \{c_n - a_n\}$ by Theorem 22. Thus $\alpha \leq \gamma$, which establishes transitivity. So far, then, we have proved that the relation is an order. That the order is linear is easy to see. For if $\{a_n\} \in \alpha$ and $\{b_n\} \in \beta$, then, by Theorem 19, $\{b_n - a_n\}$ or $\{-(b_n - a_n)\}$ is nonnegative; hence $\alpha \leq \beta$ or $\beta \leq \alpha$ ▲

The next two theorems establish the connection between the order relation and the operations of addition and multiplication.

Theorem 24

If $\alpha \leq \beta$, then $\alpha + \gamma \leq \beta + \gamma$.

Proof Let $\{a_n\} \in \alpha$, $\{b_n\} \in \beta$, and $\{c_n\} \in \gamma$. From $\alpha \leq \beta$ it follows that $\{b_n - a_n\}$ is nonnegative. But since

$$\{(b_n + c_n) - (a_n + c_n)\} = \{b_n - a_n\},$$

it follows that $\alpha + \gamma \leq \beta + \gamma$ as well ▲

Theorem 25

$\alpha \leq \beta$ and $\theta \leq \gamma$ imply $\alpha\gamma \leq \beta\gamma$.

Proof Let $\{a_n\} \in \alpha$, $\{b_n\} \in \beta$, $\{c_n\} \in \gamma$, and take $\{0\}$ as the representative of θ. From $\alpha \leq \beta$ and $\theta \leq \gamma$, it follows that both $\{b_n - a_n\}$ and $\{c_n - 0\} = \{c_n\}$ are nonnegative. Then so is $\{b_n c_n - a_n c_n\}$; hence $\alpha\gamma \leq \beta\gamma$ ▲

Finally, we establish that $\widetilde{\Re}$ is complete in this order. Proof of completeness is the only nontrivial part of the construction, and to facilitate the proof we begin by introducing some preliminary notions.

For any rational number c, the constant sequence $\{c\}$ is a Cauchy sequence and therefore must be a member of some equivalence class. Let $\varphi(c)$ be that equivalence class of which $\{c\}$ is a member. We shall refer to $\varphi(c)$ as the equivalence class *determined* by c. It is easy to see that if c and d are rational numbers, then $c \leq d$ if and only if $\varphi(c) \leq \varphi(d)$.

Theorem 26

If $\alpha \in \widetilde{\mathfrak{R}}$, then there exist integers c and d such that $\varphi(c) \leq \alpha \leq \varphi(d)$.

Proof Let $\{a_n\}$ be a member of α. Corresponding to $\varepsilon = 1$ there is an N such that

$$|a_n - a_m| < 1$$

for $n,m > N$. Select any $n' > N$ and let c and d be integers such that $c \leq a_{n'} - 1$ and $d \geq a_{n'} + 1$. Then for any $n > n'$

$$c < a_n < d$$

from which it follows that $\{a_n - c\}$ and $\{d - a_n\}$ are nonnegative ▲

If $\{c_n\}$ is a sequence, it is possible to use each member c_n to determine an equivalence class $\varphi(c_n)$. The next theorem concerns such collections of equivalence classes.

Theorem 27

Let $\{c_n\}$ and $\{d_n\}$ be Cauchy sequences and assume that $\{c_n\} \sim \{d_n\}$. If $\alpha,\beta \in \widetilde{\mathfrak{R}}$ are such that

$$\varphi(c_n) \leq \alpha \leq \beta \leq \varphi(d_n)$$

for all $n \in I_\omega$, then $\alpha = \beta$.

Proof Let $\{a_n\} \in \alpha$ and $\{b_n\} \in \beta$, and let ε be any positive number. Since $\{c_n\} \sim \{d_n\}$, there is some n' such that $|d_{n'} - c_{n'}| < \dfrac{\varepsilon}{3}$. Further, from $\varphi(c_{n'}) \leq \varphi(d_{n'})$, it follows that $c_{n'} \leq d_{n'}$ so that

$$(7) \qquad\qquad 0 \leq d_{n'} - c_{n'} < \frac{\varepsilon}{3}.$$

From $\varphi(c_{n'}) \leq \alpha$ and $\beta \leq \varphi(d_{n'})$, it follows that $\{a_n - c_{n'}\}$ and

$\{d_{n'} - b_n\}$ are nonnegative. Hence there is an N_1 such that

(8) $$-\frac{\varepsilon}{3} \le a_n - c_{n'} \quad \text{and} \quad -\frac{\varepsilon}{3} \le d_{n'} - b_n$$

for all $n > N_1$. By combining (7) and (8) it can be seen that

(9)
$$b_n - a_n \le \left(d_{n'} + \frac{\varepsilon}{3}\right) + \left(-c_{n'} + \frac{\varepsilon}{3}\right)$$
$$\le \frac{2\varepsilon}{3} + (d_{n'} - c_{n'}) < \varepsilon$$

for $n > N_1$. In addition to this, it follows from $\alpha \le \beta$ that $\{b_n - a_n\}$ is nonnegative. Hence there is some N_2 such that

(10) $$-\varepsilon < b_n - a_n$$

for $n > N_2$. If $N = \max \{N_1, N_2\}$, we conclude finally from (9) and (10) that

$$|a_n - b_n| < \varepsilon$$

for all $n > N$, hence that $\{a_n\} \sim \{b_n\}$ ▲

    With these preliminaries out of the way, we now turn to the proof of completeness.

Theorem 28

    A nonempty subset of $\widetilde{\mathfrak{R}}$ that is bounded below has an infimum.

Proof Let B be a nonempty subset of $\widetilde{\mathfrak{R}}$ and assume that B is bounded below. By using Theorem 26, it can be seen that there must be some integer c such that $\varphi(c)$ is a lower bound of B. Theorem 26 also ensures that not every integer can have this property; hence there must be a largest such integer which we call c_0. Thus $\varphi(c_0)$ is a lower bound of B while $\varphi(c_0 + 1)$ is not.

    Suppose that a rational number c_t has been chosen so that $\varphi(c_t)$ is a lower bound of B while $\varphi\left(c_t + \dfrac{1}{10^t}\right)$ is not. That is,

$$\varphi\left(c_t + \frac{n}{10^{t+1}}\right)$$

is a lower bound of B for $n = 0$ but is not a lower bound for $n = 10$. It follows that there is a largest integer n_t such that $\varphi\left(c_t + \dfrac{n_t}{10^{t+1}}\right)$ is a lower bound of B and $0 \leq n_t < 10$. We let $c_{t+1} = c_t + \dfrac{n_t}{10^{t+1}}$. Thus, by induction, we may specify a sequence $\{c_t\}$ such that, for all t,

(a) $\varphi(c_t)$ is a lower bound of B,

(b) $\varphi\left(c_t + \dfrac{1}{10^t}\right)$ is not a lower bound of B, and

(c) $c_{t+1} = c_t + \dfrac{n_t}{10^{t+1}}$ with $0 \leq n_t < 10$.

From the third condition it follows that $\{c_t\}$ is a Cauchy sequence. For, corresponding to any $\varepsilon > 0$, we may select t so that $\dfrac{1}{10^t} < \varepsilon$. From (c) it follows easily by induction that if $t < n < m$, then

$$c_t \leq c_n \leq c_m < c_t + \frac{1}{10^t},$$

hence that

$$|c_n - c_m| < \varepsilon$$

for all n and m exceeding t.

Let α be the equivalence class of which $\{c_t\}$ is a member. Since $c_t \leq c_{t+1}$ for all t, it follows that for each t_0 the sequence $\{c_t - c_{t_0}\}$ is nonnegative, and this in turn means that

(11) $\varphi(c_{t_0}) \leq \alpha$

for all t_0. Also, if $t > t_0$, then

$$c_t < c_{t_0} + \frac{1}{10^{t_0}}.$$

From this it follows that

(12) $\alpha \leq \varphi\left(c_{t_0} + \dfrac{1}{10^{t_0}}\right)$

for all t_0. Combining (11) and (12) and dropping the subscript, we thus have

(13) $$\varphi(c_t) \leq \alpha \leq \varphi\left(c_t + \frac{1}{10^t}\right)$$

for all $t \in I_\omega$.

Suppose that $\beta \in B$ and that $\beta < \alpha$. From the manner in which c_t is defined it follows that

$$\varphi(c_t) \leq \beta < \alpha \leq \varphi\left(c_t + \frac{1}{10^t}\right)$$

for all t. But obviously $\{c_t\} \sim \left\{c_t + \frac{1}{10^t}\right\}$, and this leads to a contradiction of Theorem 27. From this we conclude that $\alpha \leq \beta$ for all $\beta \in B$; in other words, α is a lower bound of B.

Finally, suppose that there is a lower bound γ of B such that $\alpha < \gamma$. Then, since $\varphi\left(c_t + \frac{1}{10^t}\right)$ is not a lower bound,

$$\varphi(c_t) \leq \alpha < \gamma \leq \varphi\left(c_t + \frac{1}{10^t}\right)$$

for all t; again this is a contradiction to Theorem 27. We conclude that α is the greatest lower bound of B; that is, α is the infimum of B ▲

This finishes the proof that $\widetilde{\mathfrak{R}}$ is a complete ordered field. Because of the uniqueness of such systems, the method of Cantor and the method of Dedekind result in the same real number system as was constructed in Chapter 6. It is easy to show that the rational subfield of $\widetilde{\mathfrak{R}}$ consists of those equivalence classes whose members converge; the remaining equivalence classes are the irrational numbers.

EXERCISES AND EXTENSIONS

1. Verify that a converging sequence $\{b_n\}$ of rational numbers satisfies the Cauchy condition.

2. Let $x_1 = 1$ and $x_{n+1} = \dfrac{2}{3 + x_n}$ for $n = 1, 2, \ldots$. Establish that $\{x_n\}$ is a Cauchy sequence of rational numbers but that it does not converge in the rational number system. [SUGGESTION: Prove that x_{n+2} lies between x_{n+1} and x_n; also that $|x_{n+1} - x_n| \leq (\frac{2}{9})^{n-1}$. Conclude from this that $\{x_n\}$ is a Cauchy sequence. Next show that a limit x of the sequence would necessarily satisfy the equation $x^2 + 3x - 2 = 0$. Conclude from this that the sequence does not converge in the rational system.]

3. Prove that the rational subfield of $\widetilde{\mathfrak{R}}$ consists of those equivalence classes whose members converge.

4. Establish the isomorphism of $\mathfrak{R}$ and $\widetilde{\mathfrak{R}}$ directly by defining an isomorphic mapping of $\mathfrak{R}$ onto $\widetilde{\mathfrak{R}}$.

5. Establish the isomorphism of $\overline{\mathfrak{R}}$ and $\widetilde{\mathfrak{R}}$ directly by defining an isomorphic mapping of $\overline{\mathfrak{R}}$ onto $\widetilde{\mathfrak{R}}$.

A *complex number* may be defined to be an ordered pair (a_1, a_2) of real numbers; let $\mathbb{C}$ be the set of all complex numbers. Two members of $\mathbb{C}$ are *equal* if and only if they are identical; thus $(a_1, a_2) = (b_1, b_2)$ if and only if $a_1 = b_1$ and $a_2 = b_2$.

6. The *sum* of complex numbers (a_1, a_2) and (b_1, b_2) is defined to be $(a_1, a_2) + (b_1, b_2) = (a_1 + b_1, a_2 + b_2)$. Prove that the resulting operation of *addition* is associative, commutative, has the *zero* $(0,0)$, and that each member of $\mathbb{C}$ has a *negative*.

7. The *product* of complex numbers (a_1, a_2) and (b_1, b_2) is defined to be $(a_1, a_2)(b_1, b_2) = (a_1 b_1 - a_2 b_2,\ a_1 b_2 + a_2 b_1)$. Prove that the resulting operation of *multiplication* is associative, commutative, has the *unit* element $(1,0)$, and that each nonzero member of $\mathbb{C}$ has an *inverse*.

8. Prove that multiplication in $\mathbb{C}$ is distributive over addition.

9. Establish that the subset of $\mathbb{C}$ consisting of all members of the form $(a,0)$ is isomorphic (relative to addition and multiplication) with the set of real numbers.

10. By verifying that $(0,1)^2 = (-1,0)$, show that the equation $x^2 + e = \theta$ has a solution in $\mathcal{C}$ [where e is the unit element and θ the zero element].

11. Prove that the set of complex numbers is not isomorphic [relative to addition and multiplication] with the set of real numbers.

12. Show that it is not possible to define a linear order in $\mathcal{C}$ so as to have the usual interactions between addition, multiplication, and order.

13. In *standard notation* the ordered pair $(0,1)$ is denoted by i; also, (x,y) is denoted by $x + iy$ since $(x,y) = (x,0) + (0,1)(y,0)$. Restate the definitions of addition and multiplication in standard notation and verify that these yield the customary rules for adding and multiplying complex numbers.

The Rational Numbers

This appendix presents, in outline, a method by which the rational number system can be constructed from the system $(I, +, \cdot \leq)$ of integers.

Let Q be the set of all ordered pairs (m,n) with $m,n \in I$ and $n > 0$. The relation $\sim$ is defined in Q by

$$(m_1,n_1) \sim (m_2,n_2) \text{ if and only if } m_1n_2 = m_2n_1.$$

It can be shown that $\sim$ is an equivalence relation; let R be the set of equivalence classes of Q that are determined by $\sim$.

For members r_1 and r_2 of R, let $(m_1,n_1) \in r_1$ and $(m_2,n_2) \in r_2$. The *sum* $r_1 + r_2$ of r_1 and r_2 is the equivalence class containing

$$(m_1n_2 + m_2n_1, n_1n_2),$$

while the *product* r_1r_2 is the equivalence class containing

$$(m_1m_2, n_1n_2).$$

Also, define a relation $\leq$ in R by stating that

$$r_1 \leq r_2 \text{ if and only if } m_1n_2 \leq m_2n_1.$$

It can be established that the above definitions are independent of the representatives of the equivalence classes that are employed; that is, they do not depend on the choice of (m_1,n_1) and (m_2,n_2). With these definitions the system $(R, +, \cdot, \leq)$ is an ordered field. The zero element is the equivalence class that contains $(0,1)$; the unit e is the class containing $(1,1)$.

Finally, if m and n are integers with n positive, it can be established that the mapping that corresponds $\dfrac{m \circ e}{n \circ e}$ with the equivalence class containing (m,n) is an isomorphism. It follows that $(R, +, \cdot, \leq)$ is the system of rational numbers.

Bibliography

Birkhoff, G., and S. MacLane: "A Survey of Modern Algebra," The Macmillan Company, New York, 1956.

Cohen, L. W., and G. Ehrlich: "Structure of the Real Number System," D. Van Nostrand Company, Inc., Princeton, N.J., 1963.

Halmos, P. R.: "Naive Set Theory," D. Van Nostrand Company, Inc., Princeton, N.J., 1960.

Kneebone, G. T.: "Mathematical Logic and the Foundations of Mathematics," D. Van Nostrand Company, Inc., Princeton, N.J., 1963.

Landau, E.: "Foundations of Analysis," Chelsea Publishing Company, New York, 1951.

McShane, E. J., and T. Botts: "Real Analysis," D. Van Nostrand Company, Inc., Princeton, N.J., 1959.

Index of Notations

ENTRIES ARE LISTED IN ORDER OF OCCURRENCE IN TEXT.

Subject Index